Journeys
in Literature and Nonfiction

Book Staff and Contributors

Margaret Thomas   *Supervising Content Specialist*
David Shireman   *Manager, Instructional Design*
Steve Mawyer   *Senior Media Editor*
Tim Mansfield   *Writer*
Susan Raley   *Text Editor*
Tricia Battipede   *Senior Creative Manager*
Jayoung Cho   *Cover Designer*
Caitlin Gildrien   *Print Visual Designer*
Sheila Smith   *Print Visual Designer, Cover Designer*

At Stride, Inc. (NYSE: LRN)—formerly K12 Inc.—we are reimagining lifelong learning as a rich, deeply personal experience that prepares learners for tomorrow. Since its inception, Stride has been committed to removing barriers that impact academic equity and to providing high-quality education for anyone—particularly those in underserved communities. The company has transformed the teaching and learning experience for millions of people by providing innovative, high-quality, tech-enabled education solutions, curriculum, and programs directly to students, schools, the military, and enterprises in primary, secondary, and post-secondary settings. Stride is a premier provider of K-12 education for students, schools, and districts, including career learning services through middle and high school curriculum. Providing a solution to the widening skills gap in the workplace and student loan crisis, Stride equips students with real world skills for in-demand jobs with career learning. For adult learners, Stride delivers professional skills training in healthcare and technology, as well as staffing and talent development for Fortune 500 companies. Stride has delivered millions of courses over the past decade and serves learners in all 50 states and more than 100 countries. The company is a proud sponsor of the Future of School, a nonprofit organization dedicated to closing the gap between the pace of technology and the pace of change in education. More information can be found at stridelearning.com, K12.com, destinationsacademy.com, galvanize.com, techelevator.com, and medcerts.com.

ISBN: 978-1-60153-514-6

Printed by Walsworth, Marceline MO, USA, May 2022.

Journeys

in Literature and Nonfiction

Table of Contents

Lessons Learned

Animals and Their People

Animal Intelligence

Mythology

On the Outside Looking In

Influential People

Human Kindness

The Impact of Words

Lessons Learned

The Stone

by Lloyd Alexander

There was a cottager named Maibon, and one day he was driving down the road in his horse and cart when he saw an old man hobbling along, so frail and feeble he doubted the poor soul could go many more steps. Though Maibon offered to take him in the cart, the old man refused; and Maibon went his way home, shaking his head over such a pitiful sight, and said to his wife, Modrona:

"Ah, ah, what a sorry thing it is to have your bones creaking and cracking, and dim eyes, and dull wits. When I think this might come to me, too! A fine, strong-armed, sturdy-legged fellow like me? One day to go tottering and have his teeth rattling in his head and live on porridge like a baby? There's no fate worse in all the world."

"There is," answered Modrona, "and that would be to have neither teeth nor porridge. Get on with you, Maibon, and stop borrowing trouble. Hoe your field or you'll have no crop to harvest, and no food for you, or me, or the little ones."

Sighing and grumbling, Maibon did as his wife **bade** him. Although the day was fair and cloudless, he took no pleasure in it. His ax blade was notched, the wooden handle splintery; his saw had lost its edge; and his hoe, once shining new, had begun to rust. None of his tools, it seemed to him, cut or chopped or **delved** as well as they once had done.

"They're as worn-out as that old codger I saw on the road," Maibon said to himself. He squinted up at the sky. "Even the sun isn't as bright as it used to be and doesn't warm me half as well. It's gone threadbare as my cloak. And no wonder, for it's been there longer than I can remember. Come to think of it, the moon's been looking a little wilted around the edges, too.

"As for me," went on Maibon, in dismay, "I'm in even a worse state. My appetite's faded, especially after meals. Mornings, when I wake, I can hardly keep myself from yawning. And at night, when I go to bed, my eyes are so heavy I can't hold them open. If that's the way things are now, the older I grow, the worse it will be!"

In the midst of his complaining, Maibon glimpsed something bouncing and tossing back and forth beside a

bade ordered
delved dug, as with a shovel

fallen tree in a corner of the field. Wondering if one of his piglets had squeezed out of the sty and gone rooting for acorns, Maibon hurried across the turf. Then he dropped his ax and **gaped** in astonishment.

There, struggling to free his leg, which had been caught under the log, lay a short, thickset figure: a dwarf with red hair bristling in all directions beneath his round, close-fitting leather cap. At the sight of Maibon, the dwarf squeezed shut his bright red eyes and began holding his breath. After a moment the dwarf's face went redder than his hair; his cheeks puffed out and soon turned purple. Then he opened one eye and blinked rapidly at Maibon, who was staring at him, speechless.

"What," snapped the dwarf, "you can still see me?"

"That I can," replied Maibon, more than ever puzzled, "and I can see very well you've got yourself tight as a wedge under that log, and all your kicking only makes it worse."

At this the dwarf blew out his breath and shook his fists. "I can't do it!" he shouted. "No matter how I try! I can't make myself invisible! Everyone in my family can disappear—poof! Gone! Vanished! But not me! Not Doli! Believe me, if I could have done, you never would have found me in such a **plight**. Worse luck! Well, come on. Don't stand there goggling like an idiot. Help me get loose!"

....

gaped stared with one's mouth open
plight a difficult situation

At this sharp command Maibon began tugging and heaving at the log. Then he stopped, wrinkled his brow, and scratched his head, saying:

"Well, now, just a moment, friend. The way you look, and all your talk about turning yourself invisible—I'm thinking you might be one of the Fair Folk."

"Oh, clever!" Doli retorted. "Oh, brilliant! Great clodhopper! Giant beanpole! Of course I am! What else! Enough gabbling. Get a move on. My leg's going to sleep."

"If a man does the Fair Folk a good turn," cried Maibon, his excitement growing, "it's told they must do one for him."

"I knew sooner or later you'd come round to that," grumbled the dwarf. "That's the way of it with you ham-handed, heavy-footed oafs. Time was, you humans got along well with us. But nowadays you no sooner see a Fair Folk than it's grab, grab, grab! Gobble, gobble, gobble! Grant my wish! Give me this, give me that! As if we had nothing better to do!

"Yes, I'll give you a favor," Doli went on. "That's the rule; I'm **obliged** to. Now, get on with it."

Hearing this, Maibon pulled and pried and chopped away at the log as fast as he could and soon freed the dwarf.

Doli heaved a sigh of relief, rubbed his shin, and cocked a red eye at Maibon, saying:

"All right. You've done your work; you'll have your reward. What do you want? Gold, I suppose. That's the

....

obliged required

usual. Jewels? Fine clothes? Take my advice, go for something practical. A hazelwood twig to help you find water if your well ever goes dry? An ax that never needs sharpening? A cook pot always brimming with food?"

"None of those!" cried Maibon. He bent down to the dwarf and whispered eagerly, "But I've heard tell that you Fair Folk have magic stones that can keep a man young forever. That's what I want. I claim one for my reward."

Doli snorted. "I might have known you'd pick something like that. As to be expected, you humans have it all **muddled**. There's nothing can make a man young again. That's even beyond the best of our skills. Those stones you're babbling about? Well, yes, there are such things. But greatly overrated. All they'll do is keep you from growing any older."

"Just as good!" Maibon exclaimed. "I want no more than that!"

Doli hesitated and frowned. "Ah—between the two of us, take the cook pot. Better all around. Those stones—we'd sooner not give them away. There's a difficulty—"

"Because you'd rather keep them for yourselves," Maibon broke in. "No, no, you shan't cheat me of my due. Don't put me off with excuses. I told you what I want, and that's what I'll have. Come, hand it over and not another word."

....

muddled mixed up; confused

Doli shrugged and opened a leather pouch that hung from his belt. He spilled a number of brightly colored pebbles into his palm, picked out one of the larger stones, and handed it to Maibon. The dwarf then jumped up, took to his heels, raced across the field, and disappeared into a thicket.

Laughing and crowing over his good fortune and his cleverness, Maibon hurried back to the cottage. There he told his wife what had happened and showed her the stone he had claimed from the Fair Folk.

"As I am now, so I'll always be!" Maibon declared, flexing his arms and thumping his chest. "A fine figure of a man! Oho, no gray beard and wrinkled brow for me!"

Instead of sharing her husband's **jubilation**, Modrona flung up her hands and burst out:

"Maibon, you're a greater fool than ever I supposed! And selfish into the bargain! You've turned down treasures! You didn't even ask that dwarf for so much as new jackets for the children! Nor a new apron for me! You could have had the roof mended. Or the walls plastered. No, a stone is what you ask for! A bit of rock no better than you'll dig up in the cow pasture!"

Crestfallen and **sheepish**, Maibon began thinking his wife was right and the dwarf had indeed given him no more than a common fieldstone.

....

jubilation tremendous joy
crestfallen feeling ashamed and humiliated
sheepish embarrassed because of some mistake

"Eh, well, it's true," he stammered; "I feel no different than I did this morning, no better or worse, but every way the same. That redheaded little wretch! He'll **rue** the day if I ever find him again!"

So saying, Maibon threw the stone into the fireplace. That night he grumbled his way to bed, dreaming revenge on the dishonest dwarf.

Next morning, after a restless night, he yawned, rubbed his eyes, and scratched his chin. Then he sat bolt upright in bed, patting his cheeks in amazement.

"My beard!" he cried, tumbling out and hurrying to tell his wife. "It hasn't grown! Not by a hair! Can it be the dwarf didn't cheat me after all?"

"Don't talk to me about beards," declared his wife as Maibon went to the fireplace, picked out the stone, and clutched it safely in both hands. "There's trouble enough in the chicken roost. Those eggs should have hatched by now, but the hen is still brooding on her nest."

"Let the chickens worry about that," answered Maibon. "Wife, don't you see what a grand thing's happened to me? I'm not a minute older than I was yesterday. Bless that generous-hearted dwarf!"

"Let me lay hands on him and I'll bless him," retorted Modrona. "That's all well and good for you. But what of me? You'll stay as you are, but I'll turn old and gray, and

....

rue to regret

worn and wrinkled, and go doddering into my grave! And what of our little ones? They'll grow up and have children of their own. And grandchildren, and great-grandchildren. And you, younger than any of them. What a foolish sight you'll be!"

But Maibon, gleeful over his good luck, paid his wife no heed and only tucked the stone deeper into his pocket. Next day, however, the eggs had still not hatched.

"And the cow!" Modrona cried. "She's long past due to calve, and no sign of a young one ready to be born!"

"Don't bother me with cows and chickens," replied Maibon. "They'll all come right, in time. As for time, I've got all the time in the world!"

Having no appetite for breakfast, Maibon went out into his field. Of all the seeds he had sown there, however, he was surprised to see not one had sprouted. The field, which by now should have been covered with green shoots, lay bare and empty.

"Eh, things do seem a little late these days," Maibon said to himself. "Well, no hurry. It's that much less for me to do. The wheat isn't growing, but neither are the weeds."

Some days went by and still the eggs had not hatched, the cow had not calved, the wheat had not sprouted. And now Maibon saw that his apple tree showed no sign of even the smallest, greenest fruit.

"Maibon, it's the fault of that stone!" wailed his wife. "Get rid of the thing!"

"Nonsense," replied Maibon. "The season's slow, that's all."

Nevertheless, his wife kept at him and kept at him so much that Maibon at last, and very reluctantly, threw the stone out the cottage window. Not too far, though, for he had it in the back of his mind to go later and find it again.

Next morning he had no need to go looking for it, for there was the stone, sitting on the window ledge.

"You see?" said Maibon to his wife. "Here it is, back again. So it's a gift meant for me to keep."

"Maibon!" cried his wife. "Will you get rid of it! We've had nothing but trouble since you brought it into the house. Now the baby's fretting and fuming. Teething, poor little thing. But not a tooth to be seen! Maibon, that stone's bad luck and I want no part of it!"

Protesting it was none of his doing that the stone had come back, Maibon carried it into the vegetable patch. He dug a hole, not a very deep one, and put the stone into it.

Next day, there was the stone, above ground, winking and glittering.

"Maibon!" cried his wife. "Once and for all, if you care for your family, get rid of that cursed thing!"

Seeing no other way to keep peace in the household, Maibon regretfully and unwillingly took the stone and threw it down the well, where it splashed into the water and sank from sight.

But that night, while he was trying vainly to sleep, there came such a rattling and clattering that Maibon clapped his hands over his ears, jumped out of bed, and went stumbling into the yard. At the well the bucket was jiggling back and forth and up and down at the end of the rope, and in the bottom of the bucket was the stone.

Now Maibon began to be truly distressed, not only for the toothless baby, the calfless cow, the fruitless tree, and the hen sitting desperately on her eggs, but for himself as well.

"Nothing's moving along as it should," he groaned. "I can't tell one day from another. Nothing changes, there's nothing to look forward to, nothing to show for my work. Why sow if the seeds don't sprout? Why plant if there's never a harvest? Why eat if I don't get hungry? Why go to bed at night, or get up in the morning, or do anything at all? And the way it looks, so it will stay for ever and ever! I'll shrivel from boredom if nothing else!"

"Maibon," pleaded his wife, "for all our sakes, destroy the dreadful thing!"

Maibon tried now to pound the stone to dust with his heaviest **mallet**, but he could not so much as knock a chip from it. He put it against his grindstone without so much as scratching it. He set it on his anvil and belabored it with hammer and tongs, all to no avail.

At last he decided to bury the stone again, this time deeper than before. Picking up his shovel, he hurried to

mallet a hammer-like tool

the field. But he suddenly halted and the shovel dropped from his hands. There, sitting cross-legged on a stump, was the dwarf.

"You!" shouted Maibon, shaking his fist. "Cheat! Villain! Trickster! I did you a good turn, and see how you've repaid it!"

The dwarf blinked at the furious Maibon. "You mortals are an ungrateful crew. I gave you what you wanted."

"You should have warned me!" burst out Maibon.

"I did," Doli snapped back. "You wouldn't listen. No, you yapped and yammered, bound to have your way. I told you we didn't like to give away those stones. When you mortals get hold of one, you stay just as you are—but so does everything around you. Before you know it, you're mired in time like a rock in the mud. You take my advice. Get rid of that stone as fast as you can."

"What do you think I've been trying to do?" blurted Maibon. "I've buried it, thrown it down the well, pounded it with a hammer—it keeps coming back to me!"

"That's because you really didn't want to give it up," Doli said. "In the back of your mind and the bottom of your heart, you didn't want to change along with the rest of the world. So long as you feel that way, the stone is yours."

"No, no!" cried Maibon. "I want no more of it. Whatever may happen, let it happen. That's better than nothing happening at all. I've had my share of being young; I'll take my share of being old. And when I come to the end of my days, at least I can say I've lived each one of them."

"If you mean that," answered Doli, "toss the stone onto the ground right there at the stump. Then get home and be about your business."

Maibon flung down the stone, spun around, and set off as fast as he could. When he dared at last to glance back over his shoulder, fearful the stone might be bouncing along at his heels, he saw no sign of it, or of the redheaded dwarf.

Maibon gave a joyful cry, for at that same instant the **fallow** field was covered with green blades of wheat, the branches of the apple tree bent to the ground, so **laden** they were with fruit. He ran to the cottage, threw his arms around his wife and children, and told them the good news. The hen hatched her chicks; the cow bore her calf. And Maibon laughed with glee when he saw the first tooth in the baby's mouth.

Never again did Maibon meet any of the Fair Folk, and he was just as glad of it. He and his wife and children and grandchildren lived many years, and Maibon was as proud of his white hair and long beard as he had been of his sturdy arms and legs.

"Stones are all right in their way," said Maibon. "But the trouble with them is, they don't grow." ❖

....

fallow inactive; plowed but with nothing growing
laden weighed down; full

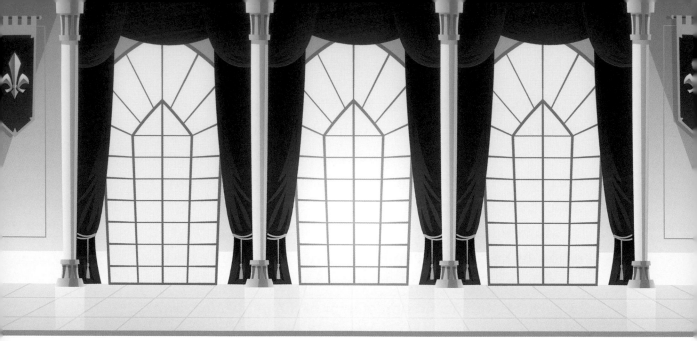

The Magic Prison

by Elizabeth Harrison

◇— Part 1 —◇

Little Harweda was born a prince. His father was king over a great land, and his mother was the most beautiful queen the world had ever seen. Prince Harweda was their only child. From the day of his birth, everything that love or money could do for him had been done.

But his parents never thought of making the young prince care for anything but himself. He had never in all his life given up one of his comforts that somebody else might have a pleasure. So, of course, he grew to be selfish; and by the time he was five years old he was so very disagreeable that nobody loved him.

"Dear, dear! What shall we do?" said the poor queen mother, and the king only sighed and answered, "Ah, what indeed!"

They were both very much grieved at heart, for they well knew that little Harweda, although he was a prince, would never grow up to be a really great king unless he could make his people love him.

At last they decided to send for his fairy godmother to see if she could find a way to cure Prince Harweda of thinking of nothing but himself.

"Well, well, well!" exclaimed the godmother, when they had laid the case before her. "This is a pretty **state of affairs**! And I his godmother, too! Why wasn't I called in sooner?"

She told them that she would have to think a day and a night and another day before she could offer them any help. "But," she added, "if I take the child in charge, you must promise not to **meddle** for a whole year."

The king and queen gladly promised that they would not speak to their son, or even see him during that time, if the fairy godmother would only cure him of his selfishness.

"We'll see about that," said the godmother. "Humph! Expecting to be a king some day and not caring for anybody but himself—a fine king he'll make!" With that, off she flew; and the king and queen saw nothing more of her for a day and a night and another day. Then back she came in a great hurry.

state of affairs a situation
meddle to interfere

"Give me the prince," said she. "I have his house all ready for him. One month from today I'll bring him back to you. Perhaps he'll be cured, and perhaps he won't. If he is not cured, then we shall try two months next time. We'll see."

Without more ado, she picked up the astonished young prince and flew away with him as lightly as if he were nothing but a feather or a straw.

They flew a long distance until they reached a great forest. When they had come to the middle of it, down flew the fairy. In a minute more the young prince was standing on the green grass beside a beautiful pink-marble palace that looked somewhat like a good-sized summerhouse.

"This is your home," said the godmother. "In it you will find everything you need, and you can do just as you choose with your time."

Little Harweda was delighted at this, for there was nothing in the world he liked better than to do as he pleased. He tossed his cap up into the air and ran into the lovely little house without so much as saying "Thank you" to his godmother.

"Humph!" she said, as he disappeared. "You'll have enough of it before you are through, my fine prince." And away she flew.

◇— Part 2 —◇

Prince Harweda had no sooner set his foot inside the small rose-colored palace than the iron door shut with a bang and locked itself. For you must know by this time that it was an enchanted house, as, of course, all houses are that are built by fairies.

His fairy godmother had told him that it was his house; therefore he was interested in looking at everything in it. From the middle of the ceiling hung a large **gilded** bird cage containing a beautiful bird, which just at this moment was singing a glad song of welcome to the prince. Harweda, however, cared very little about birds, so he took no notice of the songster.

Wonderfully carved jars and vases of gold and silver stood about the floor, and each was filled with a different kind of perfume.

"This is delicious," said Prince Harweda. "Now I can have all the sweet odors I want without the trouble of going out into the garden for flowers."

In the center of the room was a fountain of sparkling water, which leaped up and fell back into its marble basin with a faint, dreamy music very pleasant to hear.

On a table near at hand stood baskets of the most tempting pears and grapes and peaches, and near them were dishes of all kinds of **sweetmeats**.

....

gilded covered with a thin layer of gold
sweetmeats candy

"Good!" cried the greedy young prince. "That is what I like best of all." And he fell to eating the fruit and sweetmeats as fast as he could cram them into his mouth.

But, strange to say, no sooner did he reach his hand out for a soft, mellow pear or a rich, juicy peach than another pear or peach took its place.

After Prince Harweda had eaten until he could eat no more, he threw himself down on one of the couches and soon fell asleep. When he awoke he noticed for the first time the walls, which, by the way, were really the strangest part of his new home. They had in them twelve long, checkered windows which reached from the ceiling to the floor. The spaces between the windows were filled with mirrors exactly the same size as the windows, so that the whole room was walled in with windows and mirrors.

◇— Part 3 —◇

But little Prince Harweda scarcely glanced out of the windows at all, he was so taken up with the broad, handsome mirrors; for in each of them he could see himself, and he was very fond of gazing at his reflection. He was much pleased when he noticed that the mirrors were so arranged that he could see himself in several of them at the same time. He could thus see his front and back and each side all together. As he was a handsome boy, he enjoyed these many views of himself **immensely**.

immensely very much

He spent so much time gazing into the wonderful mirrors that he had very little use for the books and games that had been placed there for him. He spent hours each day before first one mirror and then another; and he did not notice that the windows were growing narrower and the mirrors wider. In fact, the windows had become so small that they hardly **admitted** light enough for him to see himself in the mirrors.

Still, this did not alarm him very much, as he cared nothing whatever for the outside world. The windows at last became mere slits in the wall, and the mirrors grew so large that they reflected not only little Harweda, but all the room besides in a dim kind of way.

Finally, however, Prince Harweda awoke one morning and found himself in total darkness. Not a ray of light came from the outside; and, of course, not an object in the room could be seen. He rubbed his eyes and sat up to make sure that he was not dreaming. Then he called loudly for someone to open a window for him, but no one came.

He got up and felt his way to the iron door and tried to open it; but, as you know, it was locked. He kicked it and beat upon it, but he only bruised his fists and hurt his toes. He grew quite angry now. How dare anyone shut him, a prince, in a dark prison like this! He cried out against his fairy godmother, calling her all sorts of horrid names.

....

admitted let in

Then he blamed his father and mother; in fact, he blamed everybody and everything but himself.

But it was of no use. The sound of his own voice was his only answer. The whole of the outside world seemed to have forgotten him.

As he felt his way back to his couch he knocked over one of the golden jars that had held the liquid perfume; the odor was all gone now, and only an empty jar rolled over the floor. He laid himself down on the couch, but its soft pillows had been removed, and an iron framework received him.

He was **dismayed**, and lay for a long time trying to think what he had best do with himself. All before him was blank darkness, as black as the darkest night you ever saw. He reached out his hand to get some fruit to eat, but only one or two **withered** apples remained on the table. Was he to starve to death?

Suddenly he noticed that the tinkling music of the fountain had ceased. He hastily felt his way over to it, and he found in place of the dancing, running stream a silent pool of water. A hush had fallen upon everything about him; a dead silence was in the room. He threw himself down upon the floor and wished that he were dead, too.

At last he heard, or thought he heard, a faint sound. He listened eagerly. It seemed to be some tiny creature not far

....

dismayed disappointed; discouraged
withered dried out

from him trying to move about. For the first time for nearly a month, he remembered the bird in its gilded cage.

"Poor little thing!" he cried, as he sprang up; "you too are shut within this terrible prison. This thick darkness must be as hard for you to bear as it is for me."

He went toward the cage, and as he came near, the bird gave a sad little chirp.

"You must need some water to drink, poor thing!" he said, filling its drinking cup. "This is all I have to give you."

Just then he heard a harsh, grating sound, as of rusty bolts sliding with difficulty out of their sockets; and then faint rays of light, not wider than a hair, began to shine between the heavy mirrors. Prince Harweda was filled with joy.

"Perhaps, perhaps," said he, softly, "I may yet see the light again. Ah, how beautiful the outside world would look to me now!"

The next day he was so hungry that he began to eat one of the old withered apples, and as he bit it he thought of the bird, his fellow prisoner.

"You must be hungry, too, poor little thing!" he said, putting part of his apple into the bird's cage.

Again came the harsh, grating sound, and the boy noticed that the cracks of light were growing larger. Still, they were only cracks; nothing of the outside world could be seen. But it was a comfort not to have to feel his way about in total darkness. Prince Harweda went up to one of the cracks and, putting his eye close to it, as he would to a pinhole in a paper, was glad to find that he could tell the greenness of the grass from the blue of the sky.

Then he climbed up into a chair and unfastened the bird cage from the golden chain by which it hung. He carried it carefully to the nearest crack of light and placed it close to the narrow opening. Once more he heard the harsh, grating sound, and the wall moved a bit; the windows were now at least an inch wide.

At this the poor prince clasped his hands with delight. He sat down near the bird cage and gazed out of the narrow opening. Never before had the trees looked so tall and **stately**, or the white clouds floating through the sky so lovely.

The next day, as he was carefully cleaning the bird's cage, the walls again creaked and groaned, and the mirrors grew narrower as the windows widened. But Prince Harweda saw only the flood of sunshine that poured in and the beauty of the larger landscape. He cared nothing whatever now for the stupid mirrors, which could only reflect what was placed before them.

One day, as two white doves suddenly soared aloft in the blue sky, the poor little bird, who had now become the prince's **comrade**, gave a pitiful little **trill**.

"Dear little fellow," cried Prince Harweda, "do you also long for your freedom? You shall at least be as free as I am." So saying, he opened the cage door and the bird flew out.

....

stately grand
comrade a friend
trill a musical sound

One day, soon after this, the little bird fluttered up against the windowpane and beat his wings against it in a **vain** effort to get out. A new idea seized the young prince. He took up a golden jar, went to the window, and struck on one of its checkered panes of glass with all his force.

"You shall be free, even if I cannot be," he said to the bird. Two or three strong blows shivered the small pane, and the bird swept out into the free air beyond.

"Ah, my pretty one, how glad I am that you are free at last!" cried the prince, watching the flight of his fellow prisoner. His face was bright with glad, unselfish joy.

The small pink-marble palace shook from top to bottom, the iron door flew open, and the fresh wind from the sea rushed in. Prince Harweda could hardly believe his eyes as he sprang to the door. There stood his fairy godmother, smiling, with her hand stretched out toward him.

"Come, my godchild," she said gently, "we will now go back to your father and mother, the king and queen."

Great indeed was the rejoicing in the palace when Prince Harweda was returned to them a changed boy, kind and thoughtful to all about him. Many a struggle he had with himself and his old habit of selfishness; but as time passed by he grew to be a great and wise king, tenderly caring for all his people, and loved by them in return. ❖

---

vain useless

Kaddo's Wall

a West African folktale
as told by Harold Courlander and George Herzog

In the town of Tendella in the Kingdom of Seno, north of
the Gulf of Guinea, there was a rich man by the name
of Kaddo. His fields spread out on every side of the town.
At plowing time hundreds of men and boys hoed up his
fields, and then hundreds of women and girls planted his
corn seed in the ground for him. His grain bulged in his
granary, because each season he harvested far more than
he could use. The name of Kaddo was known far and wide
throughout the Kingdom of Seno. Travelers who passed
through the town carried tales of his wealth far beyond
Seno's borders.

....

granary a building used to store grain

One day Kaddo called all of his people in the town of Tendella together for a big meeting in front of his house. They all came, for Kaddo was an important man, and they knew he was going to make an important announcement.

"There's something that bothers me," Kaddo said. "I've been thinking about it for a long time. I've lain awake worrying. I have so much corn in my granary that I don't know what to do with it."

The people listened attentively, and thought about Kaddo's words. Then a man said: "Some of the people of the town have no corn at all. They are very poor and have nothing. Why don't you give some of your corn to them?"

Kaddo shook his head and said, "No, that isn't a very good idea. It doesn't satisfy me."

Another man said to Kaddo, "Well, then, you could lend corn to the people who have had a bad harvest and have no seed for the spring planting. That would be very good for the town and would keep poverty away."

"No," Kaddo said, "that's no solution either."

"Well, then, why not sell some of your corn and buy cattle instead?" still another man said.

Kaddo shook his head.

"No, it's not very good advice. It's hard for people to advise a rich man with problems like mine."

Many people made suggestions, but nobody's advice suited Kaddo. He thought for a while, and at last he said,

"Send me as many young girls as you can find. I will have them grind the corn for me."

The people went away. They were angry with Kaddo. But the next day they sent a hundred girls to work for him as he had asked. On a hundred grindstones they began to grind Kaddo's corn into flour. All day long they put corn into the grindstones and took flour out. All day long the people of the town heard the sound of the grinding at Kaddo's house. A pile of corn flour began to grow. For seven days and seven nights the girls ground corn without a pause.

When the last grain of corn was ground into flour, Kaddo called the girls together and said, "Now bring water from the spring. We shall mix it with the corn flour to make **mortar** out of it."

So the girls brought water in water pots and mixed it with the flour to make a thick mortar. Then Kaddo ordered them to make bricks out of the mortar.

"When the bricks are dry, then I shall make a wall of them around my house," he said.

Word went out that Kaddo was preparing to build a wall of flour around his house, and the people of the town came to his door and protested.

"You can't do a thing like this; it is against humanity!" they said.

---

mortar a mixture used to hold bricks or stones together

"It's not right, people have no right to build walls with food!" a man said.

"Ah, what is right and what is wrong?" Kaddo said. "My right is different from yours, because I am so very rich. So leave me alone."

"Corn is to eat, so that you may keep alive," another said. "It's not meant to **taunt** those who are less fortunate."

"When people are hungry it is an affront to shut them out with a wall of flour," another man said.

"Stop your complaints," Kaddo said. "The corn is mine. It is my **surplus**. I can't eat it all. It comes from my own fields. I am rich. What good is it to be rich if you can't do what you want with your own property?"

The people of the town went away, shaking their heads in anger over Kaddo's madness. The hundred girls continued to make bricks of flour, which they dried in the sun. And when the bricks were dry Kaddo had them begin building the wall around his house. They used wet dough for mortar to hold the bricks together, and slowly the wall grew. They stuck **cowry shells** into the wall to make beautiful designs, and when at last the wall was done, and the last corn flour used up, Kaddo was very proud. He walked back and forth and looked at his wall. He walked around it. He went in and out of the gate. He was very happy.

taunt to mock
surplus an amount more than is needed; an excess
cowry shells brightly colored shells

And now when people came to see him they had to stand by the gate until he asked them to enter. When the workers who plowed and planted for Kaddo wanted to talk to him, Kaddo sat on the wall by the gate and listened to them and gave them orders. And whenever the people of the town wanted his opinion on an important matter he sat on his wall and gave it to them, while they stood and listened.

Things went on like this for a long time. Kaddo enjoyed his reputation as the richest man for miles around. The story of Kaddo's wall went to the farthest parts of the kingdom.

And then one year there was a bad harvest for Kaddo. There wasn't enough rain to grow the corn, and the earth dried up hard and dusty like the road. There wasn't a single ear of corn in all of Kaddo's fields or the fields of his relatives.

The next year it was the same. Kaddo had no seed corn left, so he sold his cattle and horses to buy corn for food and seed for a new planting. He sowed corn again, but the next harvest time it was the same, and there wasn't a single ear of corn in all his fields.

Year after year Kaddo's crops failed. Some of his relatives died of hunger, and others went away to other parts of the Kingdom of Seno, for they had no more seed corn to plant and they couldn't count on Kaddo's help. Kaddo's workers ran away, because he was unable to feed them. Gradually

Kaddo's part of the town became deserted. All that he had left were a young daughter and a **mangy** donkey.

When his cattle and his money were all gone, Kaddo became very hungry. He scraped away a little bit of the flour wall and ate it. The next day he scraped away more of the flour wall and ate it. The wall got lower and lower. Little by little it disappeared. A day came when the wall was gone, when nothing was left of the elegant structure Kaddo had built around his house, and on which he had used to sit to listen to the people of the town when they came to ask him to lend them a little seed corn.

Then Kaddo realized that if he was to live any longer he must get help from somewhere. He wondered who would help him. Not the people of Tendella, for he had insulted and mistreated them, and they would have nothing to do with him. There was only one man he could go to, Sogole, king of the Ganna people, who had the reputation of being very rich and generous.

So Kaddo and his daughter got on the mangy, underfed donkey and rode seven days until they arrived in the land of the Ganna.

Sogole sat before his royal house when Kaddo arrived. He had a soft skin put on the ground next to him for Kaddo to sit upon, and had **millet** brew brought for the two of them to drink.

....

mangy affected by a skin disease that usually causes loss of hair
millet a kind of grain

"Well, stranger in the land of the Ganna, take a long drink, for you have a long trip behind you if you come from Tendella," Sogole said.

"Thank you, but I can't drink much," Kaddo said.

"Why is that?" Sogole said. "When people are thirsty they drink."

"That is true," Kaddo replied. "But I have been hungry too long, and my stomach is shrunk."

"Well, drink in peace then, because now that you are my guest you won't be hungry. You shall have whatever you need from me."

Kaddo nodded his head solemnly and drank a little of the millet brew.

"And now tell me," Sogole said. "You say you come from the town of Tendella in the Kingdom of Seno? I've heard many tales of that town. The famine came there and drove out many people, because they had no corn left."

"Yes," Kaddo said. "Hard times drove them out, and the corn was all gone."

"But tell me, there was a rich and powerful man in Tendella named Kaddo, wasn't there? What ever happened to him? Is he still alive?"

"Yes, he is still alive," Kaddo said.

"A fabulous man, this Kaddo," Sogole said. "They say he built a wall of flour around his house out of his surplus crops, and when he talked to his people he sat on the wall by his gate. Is this true?"

"Yes, it is true," Kaddo said sadly.

"Does he still have as many cattle as he used to?" Sogole asked.

"No, they are all gone."

"It is an unhappy thing for a man who owned so much to come to so little," Sogole said. "But doesn't he have many servants and workers still?"

"His workers and servants are all gone," Kaddo said. "Of all his great household he has only one daughter left. The rest went away because there was no money and no food."

Sogole looked **melancholy**. "Ah, what is a rich man when his cattle are gone and his servants have left him? But tell me, what happened to the wall of flour that he built around his house?"

"He ate the wall," Kaddo said. "Each day he scraped a little of the flour from the wall, until it was all gone."

"A strange story," Sogole said. "But such is life."

And he thought quietly for a while about the way life goes for people sometimes, and then he asked: "And were you, by any chance, one of Kaddo's family?"

"Indeed I was one of Kaddo's family. Once I was rich. Once I had more cattle than I could count. Once I had many cornfields. Once I had hundreds of workers cultivating my crops. Once I had a bursting granary. Once I was Kaddo, the great **personage** of Tendella."

melancholy sad; gloomy
personage a notable person

"What! You yourself are Kaddo?"

"Yes, once I was proud and lordly, and now I sit in rags begging for help."

"What can I do for you?" Sogole asked.

"I have nothing left now. Give me some seed corn, so that I can go back and plant my fields again."

"Take what you need," Sogole said. He ordered his servants to bring bags of corn and to load them on Kaddo's donkey. Kaddo thanked him humbly, and he and his daughter started their return trip to Tendella.

They traveled for seven days. On the way Kaddo became very hungry. He hadn't seen so much corn for a long time as he was bringing back from the Kingdom of the Ganna. He took a few grains and put them in his mouth and chewed them. Once more he put a few grains in his mouth. Then he put a whole handful in his mouth and swallowed. He couldn't stop. He ate and ate. He forgot that this was the corn with which he had to plant his fields. When he arrived in Tendella he went to his bed to sleep, and when he arose the next morning he ate again. He ate so much of the corn that he became sick. He went to his bed again and cried out in pain, because his stomach had forgotten what to do with food. And before long Kaddo died.

Kaddo's grandchildren and great-grandchildren in the Kingdom of Seno are poor to this day. And to the rich men of the country the common people sometimes say:

"Don't build a wall of flour around your house." ❖

Harun al-Rashid & *One Thousand and One Nights*

Every so often, someone comes along whose life becomes the stuff of legend. Alexander the Great, Genghis Khan, Joan of of Arc...these figures' light shone so brightly in life that the afterglow of their **exploits** has continued for centuries after their death. Tales of their adventures and accomplishments fill both songs and stories. And even as the facts about them fade, fiction and folklore about them flourish. To this day, authors and filmmakers take on these individuals as their subjects.

Another such historical superstar was a man born in what is now Iran sometime between A.D. 763 and 766. His name was Harun al-Rashid, and, from the time of his birth, he was destined to go down in history. Born into a

exploits deeds

prominent and powerful family, al-Rashid was the second son of al-Mahdi, an important political leader. By the age of 20, al-Rashid was leading military campaigns for his father's army.

After al-Mahdi died, al-Rashid became the fifth caliph, or ruler, of an Islamic state whose capital was the city of Baghdad. He held power for more than two decades, from A.D. 786 to 809, and his empire extended from modern Morocco to India. The empire's population is estimated to have been somewhere between 20 and 30 million people. Harun al-Rashid's reign included a number of military campaigns, but it was generally peaceful. Trade and industry also grew and expanded under his rule, which made his caliphate wealthy.

Yet perhaps most importantly, during al-Rashid's rule, the Islamic world began to experience an explosion of cultural and **intellectual** growth. Libraries sprouted in cities across the caliphate, including the wonderfully named House of Wisdom in Baghdad, which al-Rashid helped found. This institution became the center of the academic world, a haven for thinkers who made advances in everything from astronomy to zoology. In fact, algebra was invented by a scholar working in the House of Wisdom.

Similarly, schools known as *madrasas* welcomed students from both near and far during al-Rashid's reign.

---

prominent important; well-known
intellectual academic; scholarly

And because knowledge and education were so prized and supported at this time—with advances made in the arts, architecture, science, and math—the Middle East developed a reputation **abroad** as a hotbed of discovery, invention, and ingenuity. Harum al-Rashid supported these developments. So, it is not surprising that his reign is widely considered to be the start of what is now known as the Islamic Golden Age.

Yet, these factors alone are not why Harun al-Rashid's name is still known today. There were other caliphs during this time. There were other figures whose deeds made an even greater impact on the world than his. So why, over 12 centuries after his death, is he remembered when others have been forgotten? Because Harun al-Rashid was made immortal through his inclusion in a collection of folktales called *One Thousand and One Nights*.

One Thousand and One Nights contains stories dripping with magic, magnificence, and mystery. A number of the tales in the collection tell about Harun al-Rashid, the loyal subjects in his court, and his **opulent** palace in Baghdad. Others focus on life in different parts of the Middle East and India, painting a vivid and memorable (if not wholly realistic) picture of a world of deep **intrigue**, fabulous adventure, and moving romance.

....

abroad in foreign countries
opulent luxurious
intrigue a secret scheme

The various individual stories within *One Thousand and One Nights* were told and collected over many decades, originally written down in Arabic during the Islamic Golden Age. Yet despite the fact that they originated in a number of different places across the Arab world, the collection is unified by an **ingenious** overall framework within the text. That framework involves a cruel king, his clever wife, and a thread that masterfully ties the diverse set of stories together.

In *One Thousand and One Nights*, King Shahrayar is a bitter man who plans to execute his new bride, Scheherazade, the morning after he marries her. Luckily, the crafty Scheherazade is aware of the king's plan, and she comes up with a strategy of her own. On their wedding night, she tells her husband a story that captivates his attention. But, knowing that he intends to have her killed the next day, she does not finish her tale.

The king, because he is so enraptured by her story, decides to delay his wife's execution so he can hear the story's conclusion the next evening. However, as soon as she finishes one tale, Scheherazade immediately begins another. Again, she captures the king's interest, and again she refuses to finish the story that night. And so it goes for one thousand and one nights, Scheherazade stringing along King Shahrayar with a series of suspenseful stories that she uses to save her own life.

....

ingenious brilliant; inventive

Within the collection, the stories that Scheherazade tells King Shahrayar vary widely. There are fables and poems, comedies and tragedies. Some tales read like early horror stories, while others feel like the **precursors** to modern mysteries. Some stories are family friendly, and some are not.

Interestingly, several of the pieces that modern readers have come to associate with *One Thousand and One Nights* were not part of the original work when it was written in Arabic. These stories include "Aladdin's Wonderful Lamp," "Ali Baba and the Forty Thieves," and "The Seven Voyages of Sinbad the Sailor." They were separate Middle Eastern folktales that were added to the collection later by European translators.

Today, *One Thousand and One Nights* gives us a fascinating glimpse into a time and culture very different from our own. It also offers us a window on a world that shaped our own in ways that many of us do not fully realize. Its fictional protagonists have become household names, and the historical figures it includes, such as Harum al-Rashid, have become icons. For these reasons and many more, *One Thousand and One Nights* has been enjoyed by adults and children all over the world for hundreds of years, and it will likely be enjoyed for hundreds more. ❖

precursors things that come before another of the same kind; forerunners

The Story of Baba Abdalla

an Arabian Nights *tale*

Once upon a time, the **caliph** Haroun al Raschid and his grand **vizier**, disguised as merchants, were proceeding across a bridge in the city of Baghdad. Along their way, they met a blind man begging for **alms**. The caliph gave him a piece of gold and was much surprised at the old man's response. "Pray, sir," said the old man, "give me a box on the ear. Otherwise I shall be unable to accept your alms, without breaking a solemn vow."

After some hesitation, the caliph obeyed this strange request, and gave the old man a very slight blow, and then continued on his walk. When they had gone a little way, the caliph said to the vizier, "Return and tell that blind man to come to my palace tomorrow at the hour of afternoon prayer, for I would hear his history, which must be strange." The vizier **hastened** to obey, and then resumed his walk with the caliph.

The next day the blind man appeared at the palace, where he was introduced into the caliph's presence by the grand vizier. He **prostrated** himself before the throne, and

caliph a Muslim leader
vizier a high-ranking Muslim official
alms charity
hastened moved quickly
prostrated bowed face down

when he rose up, the caliph asked him his name. The blind man answered that it was Baba Abdalla.

"Baba Abdalla," said the caliph, "tell me why you require those who give you alms to give you also a box on the ear."

The blind man, having bowed low, replied, "Sir, I will tell you; and you will see that this action is but a slight **penance** for a great crime of which I am guilty." Then he went on to tell this story:

I was born in Baghdad, and at an early age found myself in possession of considerable wealth. Soon I began to trade with all the cities of the land.

One of my journeys led me to Bussorah. When I was returning with my **unladen** camels, I met a **dervish**, with whom I sat down to eat.

During our meal, the dervish told me that he knew of a spot close by where there were such immense riches that, if all my **fourscore** camels were loaded with gold and jewels from it, nothing would be missed there.

I was delighted by what I heard, and begged the dervish to conduct me to the spot. Whereupon he replied, "I am ready to conduct you to the place where the treasure lies.

....

penance voluntary self-punishment to make up for some wrongdoing
unladen not weighed down
dervish a member of a Muslim religious order
fourscore eighty (one score is twenty)

We will load your fourscore camels with jewels and gold, but only if, once they are loaded, you will let me have one half, and you will be content with the other half. After that we will separate and take our camels where we may think fit. You see this is an entirely fair division, for if you give me forty camels, you will **procure**, by my help, enough to purchase thousands."

Although **avarice** made me unwilling to give up so much, I had no choice but to accept the terms the dervish offered. As soon as he had heard my decision, he led me to the place.

It was a valley situated between two high mountains, so secluded that there was no fear of discovery. When we arrived there, the dervish quickly collected some sticks and kindled a fire. As he muttered mysterious words, a dense smoke arose from the fire. When this had cleared away, I saw that the sides of the cliff had rolled back. A magnificent palace was revealed in the side of the mountain, with great heaps of treasure lying about.

Like a greedy bird of prey, I seized the gold and filled my sacks, until I saw that the dervish paid more heed to the jewels. I followed his example, so that we took away more jewels than gold. Among other things, the dervish took a small golden vase that contained nothing more

....

procure to get; to obtain
avarice greed

than a sticky ointment. And after we had loaded our camels, he closed the rock by using some **mystic** words.

We now divided the camels, each taking forty. We traveled together till we came to the great road where we were to part, the dervish to go to Bussorah, and I to Baghdad. We embraced each other with great joy, and started on our different routes.

....

mystic magical

I had not gone far before the demon of ingratitude and envy took possession of my heart. I mourned the loss of my camels, but even more the riches with which they were loaded. "The dervish," said I to myself, "has no need for all this wealth, since he is master of the treasure and may have as much as he pleases." So I gave myself up to the coldest ingratitude, and determined immediately to take from him the camels with their load.

To carry out this plan, I called to him as loudly as I could, pretending I had something important to say, and made a sign to him to stop, which he did.

When I came up to him, I said, "Brother, I had no sooner parted from you than a thought came into my head. You are used to living apart from the world, intent only upon serving God. You know not, perhaps, what trouble you have taken upon yourself, to take care of so many camels. Hear my advice and keep but thirty. You will find that number hard enough to manage. Take my word; I have had experience."

The dervish, who seemed rather afraid of me, at once had me choose ten camels from his forty. This I promptly did, and joined them with my forty.

The readiness with which he had given up these ten only increased my desire for more. "Brother," said I, "thirty camels are too many for you to manage, since you are not used to the work. Therefore I beg you relieve yourself of ten more."

My request was promptly granted by the dervish, who gave me ten more camels. He now had but twenty left, and I was master of sixty, and might boast of greater riches than any **sovereign** prince. Anyone would have thought I should now be content, but I only became greedier and more desirous of the other twenty camels.

I pleaded even more strongly in order to make the dervish grant me ten of his remaining twenty camels, which he did with good grace. And as to the ten he had left, I embraced him, kissed his feet, and begged him not to refuse me. And at length he crowned my joy by giving me them also.

Then into my head came the thought that the little vase the dervish had shown me probably contained something more precious than all the riches I had. I longed to possess it, so I said, "What will you do with that little vase of ointment? It seems such a **trifle**, it is not worth carrying away. Will you not make me a present of it? What use has a dervish, who has **renounced** the **vanities** of the world, for perfumes or scented ointments?"

Would to heaven he had refused me that vase! But if he had, I was stronger than he, and would have taken it from him by force.

....

sovereign having absolute power
trifle a small, unimportant thing
renounced given up
vanities worthless, useless things

The dervish readily pulled it out of his robe, and presented it to me with the best grace in the world, saying, "Here, take it, brother, and be content. If I can do more for you, you need but to ask me."

When I had the vase in my hand, I opened it, and said to him, "Since you are so good, I am sure you will not refuse the favor of telling me the special use of this ointment."

"The use is very surprising and wonderful," replied the dervish. "By applying a little of it around the left eye, you can at once see all the treasures contained in the earth. But if you apply it to the right eye, you will become blind."

At my request, the dervish applied the ointment to my left eye, and I found that he had indeed spoken truly. I saw vast riches and longed to grasp them all. I then bade him put some around my right eye.

"Pray remember," said the dervish, "that you will immediately become blind."

Far from being persuaded that the dervish was telling the truth, I imagined that he was trying to hide some mystery from me.

"Brother," replied I, smiling, "I see plainly you wish to mislead me. It is not natural that this ointment should have two such contrary effects."

"The matter is as I tell you," replied the dervish. "You ought to believe me, for I cannot conceal the truth."

I would not believe the dervish, although he spoke like an honest man. My great desire to possess all the treasures

in the world had such an effect on me that I would not heed
his warnings. I could not believe his words, which were,
however, all too true, as I soon found out.

Since the ointment, by being applied to the left eye, had
the power to show me all the treasures of the earth, I was
sure that, by being applied to the right, it might have the
power of giving the treasures into my hand. Possessed with
this thought, I urged the dervish to apply the ointment to
my right eye.

"Brother," said he, "after I have done you so much
service, I cannot do you so great an injury. Consider

what a misfortune it is to be deprived of one's eyesight. Do not force me to do a thing which you will be sorry for all your life."

I persisted, however, and said in strong terms, "Brother, lay aside all your objections. You have granted me all that I have asked of you **hitherto**. Would you have me go away dissatisfied about a thing of so little consequence? Grant me, I pray you, this last favor. Whatever happens, I will not lay the blame on you, but take it upon myself alone."

The dervish, having made all the resistance possible, finally took a little of the fatal ointment and applied it to my right eye. Then, alas, I immediately became blind, as you see me now.

"Ah! dervish," I exclaimed in agony, "what you warned me of has proved too true. Fatal curiosity," added I, "foolish desire of riches, into what depths of misery have they cast me! But you, dear brother, who are so charitable and good, among your wonderful secrets, have you not one that will restore to me my sight?"

"Miserable wretch!" answered the dervish, "if you had only heeded my advice, you would have avoided this misfortune, but you now have what you deserve. The blindness of your mind was the cause of the loss of your eyes. Pray to God, therefore, to restore your eyesight. He gave you riches, of which you were unworthy. On that

....

hitherto before; previously

account, he takes them from you again, and by my hands will give them to men not so ungrateful as you are."

The dervish left me to myself, overcome with despair. After he had collected my camels, he drove them away and continued on the road to Bussorah.

Thus deprived of sight and all I had in the world, I should have died with affliction and hunger, if the next day a **caravan** had not received me charitably and brought me back to Baghdad.

And so was I reduced to beggary. As a punishment for my offense, I now ask every person who gives me alms to give me also a box on the ear.

This is the explanation of what seemed so strange to your Majesty yesterday. I ask your pardon once more, and submit to whatever punishment I deserve.

"Baba Abdalla," replied the caliph, "you may cease to beg publicly, and to show my appreciation of your **remorse** and my approval of the punishment you have inflicted on yourself, I order my grand vizier to pay you daily hereafter four pieces of silver money."

At these words, Baba Abdalla prostrated himself before the caliph's throne, returned him thanks, and wished him all happiness and prosperity. ❖

....

caravan a group of people traveling together
remorse feelings of guilt and regret for the wrongs one has done

Aesop's Life

Perhaps the most famous storyteller in history, Aesop is a figure whose fables have been told and retold for millennia. Filled with beloved animal characters and memorable twists, the fables' lessons echo across generations and down through time. The fables have been brought to life in cartoons and short films. They have been referenced in poems and novels. If you've ever heard about the goose who laid the golden egg or been warned about the dangers of crying wolf, you are familiar with Aesop's fables.

Yet while the stories themselves are known the world over, relatively little is known about the life of the storyteller himself. For almost as long as the fables have been told, people have been asking the same question: Who was Aesop? It is, unfortunately, a question without a simple or conclusive answer.

In the popular imagination, Aesop is often thought of as a wise older gentleman. In paintings and sculptures, he is sometimes represented to look like Socrates or Aristotle, one in a long line of Greek thinkers whose knowledge is still valued today. Indeed, some of the earliest references to Aesop are from Aristotle and other ancient sources—Greek, Egyptian, and Roman.

These ancient sources generally agree on a few basic points regarding the historical Aesop. For one, they mostly concur that Aesop lived around 600 B.C. For another, they agree that he told the stories credited to him, often including animals or mythological figures as characters rather than people to teach simple morals to his audience. Finally, almost all sources acknowledge that Aesop himself never wrote down the fables he authored. Like other works of ancient Greek literature, such as Homer's *Iliad* and *Odyssey*, Aesop's fables were shared via word of mouth and passed down through the oral tradition.

Here, however, is where the agreement among ancient sources mostly ends. On many other matters relating to the facts of Aesop's life, there is uncertainty, contradiction, and disagreement. As a result, modern scholars must sift through texts with any number of conflicting **assertions** about Aesop in their quest to separate fact from fiction.

....

assertions claims

Some ancient sources claim that Aesop was of Ethiopian descent. Others say he was from Thrace. Some ancient authors say he lived in what is now Turkey. Others insist he resided in the city of Babylon, which was located in modern-day Iraq. Several sources, though not all, tell us that Aesop was born into slavery and was eventually freed thanks to his own cleverness.

Perhaps because the details of his life are so **shrouded** in mystery, Aesop himself became the subject of many stories over time. One of the most famous works to describe his life is *The Aesop Romance*. This text is believed to have been written in the first century of the Common Era and added to by various authors. It is not considered to be factual or a true biography, but it does weave together numerous threads from different biographical tales.

The Aesop Romance states that the **fabulist** began life as a slave on Samos, a Greek island in the Aegean Sea. It describes the young Aesop as being physically deformed and unable to speak. However, after demonstrating kindness, a goddess grants him the power to tell entertaining and meaningful stories. These fables discuss many realms of human life, including government, religion, education, health, and happiness.

shrouded surrounded
fabulist one who writes fables

However, Aesop's stories are not always shown to be sweet or harmless. They are not always the types of tales that would be told to children, as so many of Aesop's fables are today. In some instances, they are shown to be cutting or **incisive** or insulting. Some deal with issues surrounding power, politics, and ethics. The characters are often sarcastic or **caustic**. And, sometimes, telling his fables gets Aesop into trouble. For instance, the text notes that Aesop sometimes told stories that insulted the gods and goddesses of ancient Greece, which led others to view his tales as offensive and **sacrilegious**.

Nevertheless, in *The Aesop Romance*, Aesop impresses his master with his gift for telling tales. He wins respect and additional responsibility—serving for a time as his master's personal aide—before eventually gaining his freedom. Once free, the wisdom Aesop shares through his fables allows him to further improve his station in life. In the latter part of *The Aesop Romance*, Aesop serves as an adviser to several Mediterranean kings.

A particularly interesting story associated with Aesop, which appears in *The Aesop Romance* and several other works, has to do with the fabulist's death. Legend has it that Aesop was sent to the Greek city-state of Delphi as a diplomat for a king named Croesus. Croesus ruled the

incisive insightful
caustic critical in a mean-spirited way
sacrilegious disrespectful of a holy person, place, object, or idea

rival city-state of Lydia. According to the tale, Aesop tells an insulting fable to the Delphians, which results in his being falsely accused of stealing a gold or silver cup and sentenced to death.

Before being thrown off a cliff, however, Aesop warns the Delphians: His unjust execution will cause the gods to punish them. And after his warning is ignored and he is indeed killed, the Delphians do suffer from plague, **pestilence**, and brutal warfare. Thus, the story is a fitting end to one about Aesop. The lesson it teaches readers about the wrong and danger of punishing an innocent person could easily appear in one of his own fables. ❖

pestilence disease

The Shepherd's Boy and the Wolf

Aesop's Fables

A Shepherd's Boy was tending his flock near a village, and thought it would be great fun to hoax the villagers by pretending that a Wolf was attacking the sheep: so he shouted out, "Wolf! wolf!" and when the people came running up he laughed at them for their pains. He did this more than once, and every time the villagers found they had been hoaxed, for there was no Wolf at all. At last a Wolf really did come, and the Boy cried, "Wolf! wolf!" as loud as he could: but the people were so used to hearing him call that they took no notice of his cries for help. And so the Wolf had it all his own way, and killed off sheep after sheep at his leisure.

You cannot believe a liar even when he tells the truth. ❖

The Vain Jackdaw

Aesop's Fables

Jupiter announced that he intended to appoint a king over the birds, and named a day on which they were to appear before his throne, when he would select the most beautiful of them all to be their ruler. Wishing to look their best on the occasion they repaired to the banks of a stream, where they busied themselves in washing and preening their feathers. The Jackdaw was there along with the rest, and realized that, with his ugly plumage, he would have no chance of being chosen as he was: so he waited till they were all gone, and then picked up the most gaudy of the feathers they had dropped, and fastened them about his own body, with the result that he looked gayer than any of them. When the appointed day came, the birds assembled before Jupiter's throne; and, after passing them in review, he was about to make the Jackdaw king, when all the rest set upon the king-elect, stripped him of his borrowed plumes, and exposed him for the Jackdaw that he was. ❖

The Horse and the Loaded Donkey

Aesop's Fables

An idle Horse, and a Donkey laboring under a heavy burden, were traveling the road together. The Donkey, ready to faint under his heavy load, entreated the Horse to assist him, and lighten his burden, by taking some of it upon his back. The Horse was ill-natured and refused to do it; upon which the poor Donkey tumbled down in the midst of the highway, and expired. The countryman then took the whole burden, and laid it upon the Horse, together with the skin of the dead Donkey.

Laziness often prepares a burden for its own back. ❖

Animals and Their People

Zlateh the Goat

by Isaac Bashevis Singer
translated by the author and Elizabeth Shub

At Hanukkah time the road from the village to the town is usually covered with snow, but this year the winter had been a mild one. Hanukkah had almost come, yet little snow had fallen. The sun shone most of the time. The peasants complained that because of the dry weather there would be a poor harvest of winter grain. New grass sprouted, and the peasants sent their cattle out to pasture.

For Reuven the **furrier** it was a bad year, and after long hesitation he decided to sell Zlateh the goat. She was old and gave little milk. Feivel the town butcher had offered eight **gulden** for her. Such a sum would buy Hanukkah candles, potatoes and oil for pancakes, gifts for the children, and other holiday necessaries for the house. Reuven told his oldest boy Aaron to take the goat to town.

Aaron understood what taking the goat to Feivel meant, but had to obey his father. Leah, his mother, wiped the tears from her eyes when she heard the news. Aaron's younger sisters, Anna and Miriam, cried loudly. Aaron put on his quilted jacket and a cap with earmuffs, bound a rope around Zlateh's neck, and took along two slices of

---

furrier one who makes or repairs fur garments
gulden a kind of money

bread with cheese to eat on the road. Aaron was supposed to deliver the goat by evening, spend the night at the butcher's, and return the next day with the money.

While the family said goodbye to the goat, and Aaron placed the rope around her neck, Zlateh stood as patiently and good-naturedly as ever. She licked Reuven's hand. She shook her small white beard. Zlateh trusted human beings. She knew that they always fed her and never did her any harm.

When Aaron brought her out on the road to town, she seemed somewhat astonished. She'd never been led in that direction before. She looked back at him questioningly, as if to say, "Where are you taking me?" But after a while she seemed to come to the conclusion that a goat shouldn't ask questions. Still, the road was different. They passed new fields, pastures, and huts with thatched roofs. Here and there a dog barked and came running after them, but Aaron chased it away with his stick.

The sun was shining when Aaron left the village. Suddenly the weather changed. A large black cloud with a bluish center appeared in the east and spread itself rapidly over the sky. A cold wind blew in with it. The crows flew low, croaking. At first it looked as if it would rain, but instead it began to hail as in summer. It was early in the day, but it became dark as dusk. After a while the hail turned to snow.

In his twelve years Aaron had seen all kinds of weather, but he had never experienced a snow like this one. It was so dense it shut out the light of the day. In a short time their path was completely covered. The wind became as cold as ice. The road to town was narrow and winding. Aaron no longer knew where he was. He could not see through the snow. The cold soon penetrated his quilted jacket.

At first Zlateh didn't seem to mind the change in weather. She, too, was twelve years old and knew what winter meant. But when her legs sank deeper and deeper into the snow, she began to turn her head and look at Aaron in **wonderment**. Her mild eyes seemed to ask, "Why are we out in such a storm?" Aaron hoped that a peasant would come along with his cart, but no one passed by.

The snow grew thicker, falling to the ground in large, whirling flakes. Beneath it Aaron's boots touched the softness of a plowed field. He realized that he was no longer on the road. He had gone astray. He could no longer figure out which was east or west, which way was the village, the town. The wind whistled, howled, whirled the snow about in **eddies**. It looked as if white imps were playing tag on the fields. A white dust rose above the ground. Zlateh stopped. She could walk no longer. Stubbornly she anchored her **cleft** hooves in the earth and bleated as if pleading to be

wonderment amazement
eddies circular currents
cleft partially split

taken home. Icicles hung from her white beard, and her horns were glazed with frost.

Aaron did not want to admit the danger, but he knew just the same that if they did not find shelter they would freeze to death. This was no ordinary storm. It was a mighty blizzard. The snowfall had reached his knees. His hands were numb, and he could no longer feel his toes. He choked when he breathed. His nose felt like wood, and he rubbed it with snow. Zlateh's bleating began to sound like crying. Those humans in whom she had so much confidence had dragged her into a trap. Aaron began to pray to God for himself and for the innocent animal.

Suddenly he made out the shape of a hill. He wondered what it could be. Who had piled snow into such a huge heap? He moved toward it, dragging Zlateh after him. When he came near it, he realized that it was a large haystack which the snow had blanketed.

Aaron realized immediately that they were saved. With great effort he dug his way through the snow. He was a village boy and knew what to do. When he reached the hay, he hollowed out a nest for himself and the goat. No matter how cold it may be outside, in the hay it is always warm. And hay was food for Zlateh. The moment she smelled it she became contented and began to eat. Outside, the snow continued to fall. It quickly covered the passageway Aaron had dug. But a boy and an animal need to breathe, and there was hardly any air in their hideout. Aaron bored a kind of a window through the hay and snow and carefully kept the passage clear.

Zlateh, having eaten her fill, sat down on her hind legs and seemed to have regained her confidence in man. Aaron ate his two slices of bread and cheese, but after the difficult journey he was still hungry. He looked at Zlateh and noticed her udders were full. He lay down next to her, placing himself so that when he milked her he could squirt the milk into his mouth. It was rich and sweet. Zlateh was not accustomed to being milked that way, but she did not resist. On the contrary, she seemed eager to reward Aaron for bringing her to a shelter whose very walls, floor, and ceiling were made of food.

Through the window Aaron could catch a glimpse of the chaos outside. The wind carried before it whole drifts of snow. It was completely dark, and he did not know whether night had already come or whether it was the darkness of the storm. Thank God that in the hay it was not cold. The dried hay, grass, and field flowers exuded the warmth of the summer sun. Zlateh ate frequently; she nibbled from above, below, from the left and right. Her body gave forth an animal warmth, and Aaron cuddled up to her. He had always loved Zlateh, but now she was like a sister. He was alone, cut off from his family, and wanted to talk. He began to talk to Zlateh. "Zlateh, what do you think about what has happened to us?" he asked.

exuded gave off

"Maaaa," Zlateh answered.

"If we hadn't found this stack of hay, we would both be frozen stiff by now," Aaron said.

"Maaaa," was the goat's reply.

"If the snow keeps on falling like this, we may have to stay here for days," Aaron explained.

"Maaaa," Zlateh bleated.

"What does 'maaaa' mean?" Aaron asked. "You'd better speak up clearly."

"Maaaa, maaaa," Zlateh tried.

"Well, let it be 'maaaa' then," Aaron said patiently. "You can't speak, but I know you understand. I need you and you need me. Isn't that right?"

"Maaaa."

Aaron became sleepy. He made a pillow out of some hay, leaned his head on it, and dozed off. Zlateh, too, fell asleep.

When Aaron opened his eyes, he didn't know whether it was morning or night. The snow had blocked up his window. He tried to clear it, but when he had bored through to the length of his arm, he still hadn't reached the outside. Luckily he had his stick with him and was able to break through to the open air. It was still dark outside. The snow continued to fall and the wind wailed, first with one voice and then with many. Sometimes it had the sound of devilish laughter. Zlateh, too, awoke, and when Aaron greeted her, she answered, "Maaaa." Yes, Zlateh's language consisted of only one word, but it meant many things. Now she was saying, "We must accept all that God gives us—heat, cold, hunger, satisfaction, light, and darkness."

Aaron had awakened hungry. He had eaten up his food, but Zlateh had plenty of milk.

For three days Aaron and Zlateh stayed in the haystack. Aaron had always loved Zlateh, but in these three days he loved her more and more. She fed him with her milk and helped him keep warm. She comforted him with her patience. He told her many stories, and she always cocked her ears and listened. When he patted her, she licked his hand and his face. Then she said, "Maaaa," and he knew it meant, I love you, too.

The snow fell for three days, though after the first day it was not as thick and the wind quieted down. Sometimes Aaron felt that there could never have been a summer, that the snow had always fallen, ever since he could remember. He, Aaron, never had a father or mother or sisters. He was a snow child, born of the snow, and so was Zlateh. It was so quiet in the hay that his ears rang in the stillness. Aaron and Zlateh slept all night and a good part of the day. As for Aaron's dreams, they were all about warm weather. He dreamed of green fields, trees covered with blossoms, clear brooks, and singing birds. By the third night the snow had stopped, but Aaron did not dare to find his way home in the darkness. The sky became clear and the moon shone, casting silvery nets on the snow. Aaron dug his way out

and looked at the world. It was all white, quiet, dreaming dreams of heavenly splendor. The stars were large and close. The moon swam in the sky as in a sea.

On the morning of the fourth day Aaron heard the ringing of sleigh bells. The haystack was not far from the road. The peasant who drove the sleigh pointed out the way to him—not to the town and Feivel the butcher, but home to the village. Aaron had decided in the haystack that he would never part with Zlateh.

Aaron's family and their neighbors had searched for the boy and the goat but had found no trace of them during the storm. They feared they were lost. Aaron's mother and sisters cried for him; his father remained silent and gloomy. Suddenly one of the neighbors came running to their house with the news that Aaron and Zlateh were coming up the road.

There was great joy in the family. Aaron told them how he had found the stack of hay and how Zlateh had fed him with her milk. Aaron's sisters kissed and hugged Zlateh and gave her a special treat of chopped carrots and potato peels, which Zlateh gobbled up hungrily.

Nobody ever again thought of selling Zlateh, and now that the cold weather had finally set in, the villagers needed the services of Reuven the furrier once more. When Hanukkah came, Aaron's mother was able to fry pancakes

....

splendor great beauty or majesty

every evening, and Zlateh got her portion, too. Even though Zlateh had her own pen, she often came to the kitchen, knocking on the door with her horns to indicate that she was ready to visit, and she was always admitted. In the evening Aaron, Miriam, and Anna played dreidel. Zlateh sat near the stove watching the children and the flickering of the Hanukkah candles.

Once in a while Aaron would ask her, "Zlateh, do you remember the three days we spent together?"

And Zlateh would scratch her neck with a horn, shake her white bearded head, and come out with the single sound which expressed all her thoughts, and all her love. ❖

The Black Snake

by Patricia Hubbell

Black snake! Black snake!
Curling on the ground,
Rolled like a rubber tire,
Ribbed and round.
Black snake! Black snake!
Looped in a tree,
Limp as a licorice whip
Flung free.
Black snake! Black snake!
Curving down the lawn,
Glides like a wave
With its silver gone.
Black snake! Black snake!
Come and live with me!
I'll feed you and I'll pet you
And then I'll set you free! ❖

A Narrow Fellow in the Grass

by Emily Dickinson

A narrow Fellow in the Grass
Occasionally rides—
You may have met Him—did you not
His notice sudden is—

The Grass divides as with a Comb—
A spotted **shaft** is seen—
And then it closes at your feet
And opens further on—

He likes a **Boggy** Acre
A Floor too cool for Corn—
Yet when a Boy, and Barefoot—
I more than once at Noon

....

shaft a spear or pole
boggy wet or marshy

Have passed, I thought, a Whip **lash**
Unbraiding in the Sun
When stooping to **secure** it
It wrinkled, and was gone—

Several of Nature's People
I know, and they know me—
I feel for them a **transport**
Of **cordiality**—

But never met this Fellow
Attended, or alone
Without a tighter breathing
And Zero at the Bone— ❖

....

lash the end of a whip
secure to fasten in place
transport a strong emotion
cordiality friendly courtesy

The Golden Cat

by Oliver Herford

Great is the Golden Cat who treads
    The Blue Roof Garden o'er our heads,
The never tired smiling One
    That Human People call the Sun.

He stretches forth his paw at dawn
    And though the blinds are closely drawn
His claws peep through like Rays of Light,
    To catch the fluttering Bird of Night.

He smiles into the Hayloft dim
    And the brown Hay smiles back at him,
And when he strokes the Earth's green fur
    He makes the Fields and Meadows purr.

His face is one big Golden smile,
    It measures round, at least a mile—
How dull our World would be, and flat,
    Without the Golden Pussy Cat. ❖

The Cat and the Moon

by William Butler Yeats

The cat went here and there
And the moon spun round like a top,
And the nearest **kin** of the moon,
The creeping cat, looked up.
Black Minnaloushe stared at the moon,
For, wander and **wail** as he would,
The pure cold light in the sky
Troubled his animal blood.
Minnaloushe runs in the grass
Lifting his delicate feet.
Do you dance, Minnaloushe, do you dance?
When two close **kindred** meet,
What better than call a dance?
Maybe the moon may learn,
Tired of that **courtly** fashion,
A new dance turn.
Minnaloushe creeps through the grass
From moonlit place to place,
The sacred moon overhead
Has taken a new phase.

kin a relative; a family member
wail to cry loudly
kindred relatives; family members
courtly noble or elegant

Does Minnaloushe know that his **pupils**
Will pass from change to change,
And that from round to **crescent**,
From crescent to round they range?
Minnaloushe creeps through the grass
Alone, important and wise,
And lifts to the changing moon
His changing eyes. ❖

....

pupils centers of the eyes
crescent the shape of the moon when it is very thin

Stray

by Cynthia Rylant

In January, a puppy wandered onto the property of
Mr. Amos Lacey and his wife, Mamie, and their daughter,
Doris. Icicles hung three feet or more from the **eaves** of
houses, snowdrifts swallowed up automobiles, and the birds
were so fluffed up they looked comic.

The puppy had been abandoned, and it made its way
down the road toward the Laceys' small house, its ears
tucked, its tail between its legs, shivering.

Doris, whose school had been called off because of the
snow, was out shoveling the cinder-block front steps when
she spotted the pup on the road. She set down the shovel.

"Hey! Come on!" she called.

The puppy stopped in the road, wagging its tail timidly,
trembling with shyness and cold.

Doris trudged through the yard, went up the shoveled
drive, and met the dog.

"Come on, pooch."

"Where did that come from?" Mrs. Lacey asked as soon
as Doris put the dog down in the kitchen.

Mr. Lacey was at the table, cleaning his fingernails with
his pocketknife. The snow was keeping him home from his
job at the warehouse.

....

eaves the part of a roof that hangs over the wall

"I don't know where it came from," he said mildly, "but I know for sure where it's going."

Doris hugged the puppy hard against her. She said nothing.

Because the roads would be too bad for travel for many days, Mr. Lacey couldn't get out to take the puppy to the pound in the city right away. He agreed to let it sleep in the basement, while Mrs. Lacey **grudgingly** let Doris feed it table scraps. The woman was sensitive about throwing out food.

By the looks of it, Doris figured the puppy was about six months old and on its way to a big dog. She thought it might have some shepherd in it.

Four days passed and the puppy did not complain. It never cried in the night or howled at the wind. It didn't tear up everything in the basement. It wouldn't even follow Doris up the basement steps unless it was invited.

It was a good dog.

Several times Doris had opened the door in the kitchen that led to the basement, and the puppy had been there, all stretched out, on the top step. Doris knew it had wanted

....

grudgingly reluctantly, unwillingly

some company and that it had lain against the door, listening to the talk in the kitchen, smelling the food, being a part of things. It always wagged its tail, eyes all sleepy, when she found it there.

Even after a week had gone by, Doris didn't name the dog. She knew her parents wouldn't let her keep it, that her father made so little money any pets were out of the question, and that the pup would definitely go to the pound when the weather cleared. Still, she tried talking to them about the dog at dinner one night.

"She's a good dog, isn't she?" Doris said, hoping one of them would agree with her.

Her parents glanced at each other and went on eating.

"She's not much trouble," Doris added. "I like her." She smiled at them, but they continued to ignore her.

"I figure she's real smart," Doris said to her mother. "I could teach her things."

Mrs. Lacey just shook her head and stuffed a forkful of sweet potato in her mouth. Doris fell silent, praying the weather would never clear.

But on Saturday, nine days after the dog had arrived, the sun was shining and the roads were plowed. Mr. Lacey opened up the trunk of his car and came into the house.

Doris was sitting alone in the living room, hugging a pillow and rocking back and forth on the edge of a chair. She was trying not to cry but she was not strong enough. Her face was wet and red, her eyes full of distress.

Mrs. Lacey looked into the room from the doorway.

"Mama," Doris said in a small voice. "Please."

Mrs. Lacey shook her head.

"You know we can't afford a dog, Doris. You try to act more grown-up about this."

Doris pressed her face into the pillow.

Outside, she heard the trunk of the car slam shut, one of the doors open and close, the old engine cough and choke and finally start up.

"Daddy," she whispered. "Please."

She heard the car travel down the road, and though it was early afternoon, she could do nothing but go to her bed. She cried herself to sleep, and her dreams were full of searching and searching for things lost.

It was nearly night when she finally woke up. Lying there, like stone, still exhausted, she wondered if she would ever in her life have anything. She stared at the wall for a while.

But she started feeling hungry, and she knew she'd have to make herself get out of bed and eat some dinner. She wanted not to go into the kitchen, past the basement door. She wanted not to face her parents.

But she rose up heavily.

Her parents were sitting at the table, dinner over, drinking coffee. They looked at her when she came in, but she kept her head down. No one spoke.

Doris made herself a glass of powdered milk and drank it all down. Then she picked up a cold biscuit and started out of the room.

"You'd better feed that mutt before it dies of starvation," Mr. Lacey said.

Doris turned around.

"What?"

"I said, you'd better feed your dog. I figure it's looking for you."

Doris put her hand to her mouth.

"You didn't take her?" she asked.

"Oh, I took her all right," her father answered. "Worst-looking place I've ever seen. Ten dogs to a cage. Smell was enough to knock you down. And they give an animal six days to live. Then they kill it with some kind of a shot."

Doris stared at her father.

"I wouldn't leave an ant in that place," he said. "So I brought the dog back."

Mrs. Lacey was smiling at him and shaking her head as if she would never, ever, understand him.

Mr. Lacey sipped his coffee.

"Well," he said, "are you going to feed it or not?" ❖

Playing Robinson Crusoe

by Rudyard Kipling

Pussy can sit by the fire and sing,
    Pussy can climb a tree,
Or play with a silly old cork and string
    To 'muse herself, not me.
But I like Binkie, my dog, because
    He knows how to behave;
So, Binkie's the same as the First Friend was
    And I am the Man in the Cave.

Pussy will play Man-Friday till
    It's time to wet her paw
And make her walk on the window-sill
    (For the footprint Crusoe saw);
Then she fluffles her tail and mews,
    And scratches and won't attend.
But Binkie will play whatever I choose,
    And he is my true First Friend.

Pussy will rub my knees with her head,
    Pretending she loves me hard;
But the very minute I go to my bed
    Pussy runs out in the yard,
And there she stays till the morning light;
    So I know it is only pretend;
But Binkie, he snores at my feet all night,
    And he is my Firstest Friend! ❖

Lone Dog

by Irene Rutherford McLeod

I'm a lean dog, a **keen** dog, a wild dog, and lone;
I'm a rough dog, a tough dog, hunting on my own;
I'm a bad dog, a mad dog, teasing silly sheep;
I love to sit and **bay** the moon, to keep fat souls from sleep.
I'll never be a lap dog, licking dirty feet,
A sleek dog, a meek dog, **cringing** for my meat,
Not for me the fireside, the well-filled plate,
But shut door, and sharp stone, and **cuff** and kick, and hate.
Not for me the other dogs, running by my side,
Some have run a short while, but none of them would **bide**.
O mine is still the lone trail, the hard trail, the best,
Wide wind, and wild stars, and the hunger of the quest! ❖

keen sharp; clever
bay to howl
cringing shrinking in fear
cuff a slap
bide to last

Animal Intelligence

Are Dogs Dumb?

by Karen Hopkin

Chimps can use sign language to talk to their trainers. Monkeys can learn to count. A crow can figure out how to use a stick to get at that hard-to-reach grub. Chickens can learn to play checkers. Even worms can be taught to run mazes. So which animal is the smartest? You're probably thinking that chimps are smarter than chickens. And that crows are smarter than worms. And that you're smarter than all of them.

But where do those rankings come from? Okay, you probably are smarter than the average worm. But why do we assume that bigger beasts are smarter than smaller ones? Or that furry critters are brainier than slithering wrigglers that are coated in slime?

And how come we think dogs are so smart? Sure a dog might be clever enough to fetch his leash when he wants to go out. But the same mutt might also bark at vacuum cleaner and spend a whole hour chasing his own tail. Is Rover really any brighter than a hamster, a chicken, or that kid who's always eating Play-Doh? How can you measure an animal's brain power?

The hardest part is coming up with the right test. A dog can't sit down with a No. 2 pencil and take a multiple choice exam. So the test has to be something the dog can learn to do: select a block by nudging it with a nose or a paw, for example. The test also has to be something the dog *wants* to do: a dog might stare at that block all day without budging—until she figures out that there's a treat hidden underneath.

Norton Milgram and his coworkers at the University of Toronto at Scarborough use treats to give dogs a Canine IQ test. The dog is presented with a tray with a blue block on it; underneath the block is a treat. The animal moves the block and gets the treat. So far, so good. Now the test gets tricky. The dog is presented with the same tray, but this time it has both a blue block and a yellow coffee can lid (or white bowl or black square of cloth) on it; the treat is now under the yellow lid (or white bowl, etc.). The test: how long does it take for the dog to learn that the treat is always under the new item on the tray? The smarter the dog, the quicker she'll find the treat. That seems simple enough, but things become more complicated when you try to compare different kinds of animals. Monkeys wipe the floor with dogs on this test.

Dogs may have to try hundreds of times before they select the yellow lid nine out of ten times. Monkeys learn much more quickly to find the hidden treat. Does that mean monkeys are smarter than dogs?

Not necessarily. The test was originally designed for monkeys, and it gives them an unfair advantage: by nature monkeys are curious and like to check out new things. Dogs, on the other hand, tend to be wary about approaching new things. As Stephen Budiansky reports in his book *The Truth about Dogs*, one pooch was so scared of the yellow lid that he had to be excused from the study.

If the test is made more dog-friendly, on the other hand, canines do just fine. Instead of introducing a yellow lid, the treat is put under another blue block on the opposite side of the tray. Dogs learn as quickly as any monkey that the treat is always on the side opposite the first block they saw.

Even if you could find a test that was perfectly fair to all animals, in a way it's silly to ask whether one kind of animal is smarter than another. All animals have the ability to learn things that are important to them. Otherwise they wouldn't survive. A chicken doesn't need to be a chess champion to figure out where to get food or how to run from a predator. So a chicken is as smart as it needs to be to earn a living as a chicken.

If you still believe that dogs are much smarter than chickens, it's probably because dogs are good at learning the things we want them to learn: fetching the newspaper, for example. Try to convince a chicken to do that! The truth is, most dog tricks take advantage

of dogs' built-in behavior patterns—things that dogs are born knowing how to do or learn easily. Chasing and retrieving are leftover hunting behaviors. For a dog, fetching the paper or a tennis ball is not a reflection of intelligence. It's basically a demonstration that dogs will be dogs.

Canines may not be the deepest thinkers in the world. But perhaps that's for the best. The life of a dog—sitting alone all day, waiting for everyone to come home—can be pretty boring. Super-smart animals would probably get totally stressed out, says University of Pennsylvania researcher James Serpell. Look at it this way: if dogs were any smarter, they probably wouldn't choose to hang around with us. ❖

Karen Hopkin is a science writer living in Somerville, Massachusetts. She growls quite a bit, but barks only on request.

Dog Talk

Listen. Do you hear it? No matter where you are, if you stick your head out a window for a minute or two you'll probably hear a dog barking. What is it they're trying to say? Does that racket actually mean something? Why do dogs bark?

"It depends on who you ask," says Nicholas Dodman of Tufts Veterinary School in Massachusetts. "Some say dogs bark because they can." Unlike dogs, adult wolves—our canine pals' ancestors—don't really bark. "They don't say much of anything," says Ray Coppinger of Hampshire College in Massachusetts. So barking seems to be something dogs have picked up since they were tamed. Maybe they've learned it can be useful for getting attention, like tooting on a car horn, says Dodman: it's an all-purpose "Hey, I'm here! Look at me!"

But not all barks are alike. That happy "going for for a walk" yap can sound very different from the threatening "stranger at the door" snarl. So maybe barks do have different meanings. Sophia Yin tried to find out. As a student at the University of California in Davis, Yin recorded the sound of dogs barking in three situations: when a doorbell rang;

while playing with a tennis ball; and when shut out of the house. She then analyzed some 4,500 barks on her computer, rating them according to their loudness, harshness, and pitch (whether they sound high—arf arf—or low—woof woof).

Yin found that the barks were different. The doorbell barks were harsher and deeper, for example, whereas play barks were pitched higher. But just because her computer can tell the difference between one woof and another doesn't mean dogs can. "We need to do a playback study," says Yin, "to see if the dogs respond the right way"—getting excited when they hear a playful ruff or upset when they hear the menacing doorbell bow-wow.

Of course, maybe barking isn't supposed to mean anything to dogs—just to their masters. After all, that's who dogs talk to most. A Japanese toy company is trying to take advantage of that possibility by selling a small recorder that clips onto a dog's collar and "translates" its barking for you. A special pager will let you know whether Fido is happy, sad, frustrated, or alarmed.

That's probably stretching it, says Yin. Without seeing the dog, it's hard to say whether a particular ruff means "more kibbles, please" or "yeah, I ate your shoe." Still, even though barking isn't a complex language, it probably does mean something. And dogs will continue to bark as long as barking brings results. "When a dog barks at the mailman, he always goes away," notes James Serpell of the University of Pennsylvania. "It's very reinforcing." –K. H.

Farallon Islands along the Pacific coast

The Day the Gulls Went Crazy

by Susan E. Quinlan

Until they turned on him, Larry Spear was on friendly terms with his research subjects. A bird scientist, Larry had spent nearly a decade studying western gulls—trying to learn the secrets of their lives. He had visited them at their nesting islands, handled their eggs and young, and tracked them in their winter journeys along the Pacific coast. He was used to mixing with them freely.

But in the summer of 1980, when Larry walked out of the research building on Southeast Farallon Island, about 30 miles west of San Francisco, the gulls were no longer friendly. In an uproar of amazing **proportions**,

....

proportions size

over 8,000 of the 25,000 gulls nesting on the island began screaming and dive-bombing him. Many offloaded gooey white droppings with missile-like accuracy.

At first, Larry thought the angry display would die down. Instead, it got worse. The loud piercing cries of the whirling gulls caused a **frenzied** stampede of Steller's sea lions from their pupping area. Shaken and worried, Larry hurried back inside the house to puzzle over this new and decidedly unfriendly reception from his study subjects.

Like most gulls, western gulls nest in colonies. This means that many pairs place their nests close together in a particular place. In contrast, most bird species place their nests in scattered, hidden locations. Colonial nesting is an unusual habit among birds because predators can easily locate nests placed close together and quickly eat many eggs and young. In general, colonial birds nest in places out of reach of predatory mammals, such as cliff ledges, river sand bars, and isolated ocean islands.

Most colonial birds also defend their nests by "mobbing" predators. When one bird in a colony spots a predator, it flies up and sounds an alarm. All the nearby birds then fly up and give alarm calls too. If the alarm is strong enough, it travels through the colony like a wave. Soon most of the birds in the colony are airborne. The alarmed birds scream, dive-bomb, and harass the predator to drive it away. People who walk near colonies of nesting birds often get

frenzied wild and panicked

mobbed in the same way that a fox, a coyote, or an eagle might. The gulls' reaction to Larry was nothing more than an intense display of their natural behavior toward a feared predator.

However, none of the scientists working at Southeast Farallon Island could remember western gulls reacting to a person with such alarm. Several scientists from the Point Reyes Bird Observatory live and work on the island year-round. And for the most part, the gulls had always ignored them. Even gulls nesting next to foot trails remained calm when people passed within a few feet of their nests. So the gulls' mobbing response to Larry surprised everyone. Larry felt stunned by its **intensity**. But when he thought about it, he knew what had happened.

Larry had begun studying the gulls of Southeast Farallon Island in 1971, nine years before the mobbing incident. Since all western gulls look alike to people, Larry needed a way to identify individual birds. So he and his coworkers began putting leg bands on the gulls. Late in the nesting season each year, banders entered the gulls' nesting colony and banded chicks from as many nests as possible. Though the chicks and brooding (or nesting) adults occasionally protested mildly, Larry and his coworkers were able to measure and band the chicks without causing any great disturbances in the colony.

Each chick was fitted with a numbered aluminum leg band from the U.S. Fish and Wildlife Service and a colored plastic leg band to indicate the hatching year. Banders carefully recorded

intensity force

Banding chicks

the numbers on each metal band along with information about that chick. From 1971 to 1979, Larry and other workers banded about 18,000 western gull chicks.

These individually identifiable birds gave Larry a chance to **unravel** the secrets of gull life. If he got a good look at the leg of any banded gull, Larry could read the band number, look back through his records, and tell exactly when and where on the Farallon Islands the bird had hatched and who its parents were. Even if he couldn't get a close look, the colored plastic band revealed the year the bird was hatched.

By 1978, observations of these marked gulls were just beginning to yield some

unravel to find the right answer or explanation

interesting information. Some of the birds banded in the early 1970s returned to nest revealing that western gulls start nesting at age four or five. Larry discovered that his banded gulls eventually nested quite close to the site where they had hatched. Larry felt particularly excited when he began to learn a bit about the wandering winter lives of the Farallon Island gulls.

To discover their secrets, Larry went on a real-life scavenger hunt each winter. He traveled up and down the Pacific coast, looking for marked birds. He visited docks, fish canneries, restaurant parking lots, garbage dumps, and other sites where hungry gulls might be looking for a meal. It might sound easy to find some of the thousands of banded gulls, but there are probably more than 100,000 adult and young western gulls along the Pacific coast. So Larry had to work hard to find his banded ones.

Over the years, Larry figured out ways to increase the odds of identifying banded birds. He began carrying buckets of dead fish in his car trunk. Whenever he saw any western gulls, he began throwing out fish parts to lure them closer in hopes of spotting any bands. When he saw a banded bird, he got out his spotting scope and focused it on the bird's leg. Sometimes he tossed fish parts around the bird so that it would turn in a circle and allow him to read the numbers on its leg band. Through hard work and cleverness, Larry learned that western gull chicks from the Farallon Islands spend winter apart from their parents. He also figured out that some gull pairs enjoy separate winter vacations, with the male and female heading in different directions along the coast. Such tidbits of information made him even more eager to learn about the secret lives of gulls.

Larry knew that he'd learn more and more about the gulls' lives as more and more banded chicks grew into adults and began to nest. But in 1978, he made an unsettling discovery. Many of the aluminum bands placed on birds in the early 1970s had become so worn that the band numbers were now hard to read. Even worse, some aluminum bands were falling off. Years of effort and information would be lost, if he didn't quickly figure out a way to replace the worn bands.

Capturing and rebanding an adult gull is much more difficult than capturing a small flightless chick. Resourceful as always, Larry developed a special capture technique. He rigged up a tool using a rope noose, **monofilament** fishing line, and a fishing pole. Knowing the fight a two-and-a-half-pound adult gull might put up, he scared the bird off its nest and replaced its fragile eggs with dummy eggs. Next, he laid the noose around the nest and moved away. A trail of fishing line led from the noose to the fishing pole and reel in his hands. Crouching low, Larry waited for the return of the bird in need of rebanding. When the moment was right, he reeled in the line, tightening the noose around the gull's legs.

As Larry expected, the recaptured gulls weren't too happy about being treated this way, and they let everyone know it. Nearby gulls reacted to the captured birds' distress

....

monofilament a thin, single strand of nylon

by flying up and crying in alarm. Larry worked quickly. He weighed and rebanded his captive, replaced the real eggs, then released the bird and moved away. After each localized alarm, calm returned to the colony. In 1979, Larry noosed only one or two birds every few days and captured them in well-separated parts of the colony. This method kept the gulls' response to a minimum.

But in 1980, Larry had less time to reband birds. Under pressure, he trapped nine different birds in two days— each time exciting a bit of panic. To his surprise, this rebanding effort proved too much for the gulls. When Larry set foot outside the research house the next day, thousands of gulls went **berserk**. Larry was extremely worried. The gulls' reaction meant that he couldn't reband other gulls, band any new chicks, or learn anything more about the nesting gulls that year. Even worse, since the screaming gulls had triggered a stampede of Steller's sea lions and greatly disturbed other nesting seabirds, any appearance by Larry posed a serious threat to the safety of the island's wildlife. He didn't dare step outside.

Frustrated, Larry and his coworkers discussed the problem. Curiously, the gulls did not react to other people. Other researchers could come and go from the house as they pleased. Obviously the gulls could identify Larry in some way. In their eyes, he had some marking that made him stand out from all the other people on

berserk actions that are wild, violent, and reckless

the island. But what was it? His hat? His coat? His body shape? His walk?

An experiment seemed the best way to answer this question. Larry rigged up a disguise from spare items around the house. Instead of his usual yellow stocking cap, he wore a wide-brimmed straw hat. He changed into baggy clothing that he had never worn before. And to top off the disguise, he added a green and orange Halloween mask left behind from some party. In this outfit, Larry walked out of the house, being careful to change his walk by pretending to limp. To his amazement, the colony stayed perfectly calm. Since he didn't want to wear this costume and limp around for the rest of his stay on the island, Larry began trying out different versions of his get-up. He tried wearing his regular clothes, but kept on the mask and straw hat and walked normally. No reaction from the gulls. They didn't recognize him by his pants, coat, or his walk.

He tried again. This time he wore his regular clothes and normal yellow hat, but still wore the mask. A mild alarm resulted. He tried once more. Still wearing the mask, he put on his regular clothes and a similar-style gray hat. The gulls stayed calm. Now Larry thought he had figured out how the gulls recognized him. He decided to make one final test.

Back inside, he took off the mask, put the baggy clothes and wide-brimmed straw hat back on, and limped outside. Gull **pandemonium** began promptly. Despite his disguising

---

pandemonium chaos

clothes and limp, the gulls instantly recognized Larry. They knew him by his face—the same feature we use to recognize one another.

Larry was forced to wear the gray cap and Halloween mask every time he left the house in 1980. Amazingly, a year later when he returned for another nesting season, many gulls still remembered his face and again reacted in alarm. From then on, researchers always wore masks when rebanding gulls. This was necessary to prevent the gulls from identifying any other researcher as an enemy.

"The whole incident added a new dimension to my respect for these birds," Larry says. But he adds that we shouldn't be too surprised by the ability of gulls to recognize people by their faces. "After all," he points out, "gulls can recognize their mates at a distance of one hundred feet and identify nesting neighbors on sight. These feats are all the more impressive when you consider that the only way we humans can tell one gull from any other is by marking them with numbered bands."

Clearly "bird brains" are more complicated than we think. And perhaps, we humans aren't so smart after all. That's something to think about the next time you watch a bird. And if you see some gulls, think twice before you disturb them. They just might remember your face. And as Larry can tell you, they dive-bomb with missile-like accuracy. ❖

The Think Tank

by Patricia Daniels

Azy, a 21-year-old male orangutan, had been scoring 100 percent on the day's vocabulary test—until now. National Zoo biologist Rob Shumaker holds up some folded bags containing chopped fruit. "Okay, Azy, want to tell me what this is?" In front of the rusty-haired ape is a computer screen showing some symbols. Each one stands for a word. Azy lifts his long, graceful hand and points to the symbol for cup. A buzzer sounds. The screen shows an hourglass symbol that means his answer is wrong.

For the first time this afternoon, Azy seems confused. Shumaker shows him the bags again, and again the orang points to "cup." On the fourth try, Azy figures it out. He points to the symbol for "bag," and Shumaker hands him the paper bags through an opening in the **Plexiglas** between them. Azy picks out the fruit and

Dr. Rob Shumaker explains the symbols that Azy knows well to an audience at the International Orangutan Center.

Plexiglas a see-through type of plastic often used in place of glass reluctantly hands back the bags when the biologist asks politely, "Azy, can I have those?"

For the last three years, Shumaker has been working with Azy and five other orangutans at the zoo's Think Tank building. In addition to these great apes, Think Tank researchers are studying creatures as various as hermit crabs, leafcutter ants, and **macaques**. They hope to learn whether—and how—animals think. Some of the scientists look at tool use. Others observe the animals' social life. Shumaker would like to know if orangutans can learn language.

Shumaker is delighted with Azy's mistake. "Azy's mistakes are more interesting than his right answers," he says. "When he saw the bags, he didn't pick a symbol that meant food, such as 'apple.' He didn't pick a verb, such as 'open.' He picked the one other symbol that meant an object, a container. I think his mistakes show that he's putting these words into categories in his mind. Maybe this can teach us a little bit about how he thinks."

Shumaker has known most of the zoo's orangs since they were born. "Orangs' mental abilities are the least understood of the great apes," notes the biologist. "We want to learn more about them, mentally. We also want to add to the quality of their lives by giving them some challenges, some mental enrichment. They all take part in the project voluntarily. None of them is ever forced or punished."

"The most important thing to know is that they are all

---

macaques a type of Asian monkey

individuals," he adds. "Just like people, they have different personalities and learning styles. When we started the project, I didn't think Azy would be the fastest learner. But I was wrong. For instance, though he doesn't use tools as much as the other orangs, Azy has turned out to be the best language student. He is very focused and hardworking. I can see him steadily building his knowledge, step by step, making connections."

What's the next step? "We're going to start putting words together into simple sentences," says Shumaker. "Then things will really get interesting." ❖

Azy selects the right answer.

Close Encounters of the Bear Kind

by Susan E. Quinlan

Beep…beep…beep…beep. The quickening beeps of the radio signal tell John Hechtel two things. He's getting close to a bear den and the bear inside is waking up. Bears lower their body temperature less than other hibernators, so they're easily awakened. John and his coworkers crunch loudly as they snowshoe across the crusty snow. Bowed-down branches of willow shrubs weave a carpet of shadows over the snow, making it tough to spot the small breathing hole that usually marks a bear's den. The scientists look carefully and move slowly. It's not a good idea to step on a bear that's just woken up.

John is a biologist with the Alaska Department of Fish and Game. His study area is the Tanana Valley, a **boggy** lowland in central Alaska. It's prime black bear habitat, but most of the ground is too wet for dens. Unfortunately, the only dry areas that seem good for dens also happen to be used by the U.S. Army for winter training. So to protect both bears and soldiers, the army hired John to find out where most bears in the area **hibernate**.

John spent last summer fitting bears with radio collars like the one that is now leading him to a den. The collar has a **transmitter** that sends out a beep John can track to its

boggy wet, spongy
hibernate to sleep or be inactive through the winter
transmitter equipment that sends out radio signals

source. It also has an activity sensor that speeds up the beeps when the bear moves.

John has captured bears in traps made from 55-gallon drums. He's also darted some from the air. Darting a bear from the open door of a helicopter—held in by just a seat belt or climbing harness—sounds challenging. But John says, "No, it's not if I have a good pilot. If I'm worried about the helicopter **rotors** getting too close to the treetops, then it is tough to focus. But if I trust the pilot, it's fairly simple. The more difficult part is following the bear afterward. It takes from three to eight minutes for the drug to take full effect. We have to keep close enough to watch the bear without making it panic. If the bear falls into water, then I have to get down right away and make sure its head stays up, so it doesn't drown."

John and his coworkers calmly close in on this sleeping bear. The beeping signal is now strong and fast. John spots a small hole in the snow that he figures may mark the den

rotors the blades of a helicopter

entrance. Before moving in, he pulls a sleeping bag out of his pack. Holding it in one hand, he advances. The blinding glare of spring sunlight glinting off the snow makes it tough to make out where the bear is in the hole. John crouches down, shades his eyes with his hands and puts his face close to peer inside. With a startled look, he pulls back and whips the sleeping bag over the hole. The black bear inside is not only awake; its head is right at the entrance. John hopes the sleeping bag will keep the den dark and the bear calm a bit longer. He carefully readies a drug-filled hypodermic needle mounted on a short stick. It will take good aim and a quick

Bear Crazy

John grew up in suburban Chicago in a family that didn't much like the outdoors. When he was 13, he saw a National Geographic television program about bear research. It inspired him to apply to a summer school program at the University of Montana, where he met the scientists who were on TV.

John eventually went to college at the University of Montana, where he took care of some captive bears for the same scientists. After college, he joined the Peace Corps and went to Cameroon in Africa. There he got interested in the **conservation** of African wildlife and hoped to make that his specialty. But a motorcycle accident cost him his spleen, making it dangerous for him to work in the tropics.

....
conservation protection of animals and natural resources

jab to poke the needle into the bear's shoulder muscle.

Fortunately John has had practice, so this bear is drugged safely. He and his coworkers then measure the bear and the den. They return the bear to its sleeping hole after a half hour. Occasionally, they don't return the bear. Instead, they take it to an artificial den at the University of Alaska, where other scientists can study its hibernation more easily.

John has tracked down quite a few bear dens—about 100, he thinks. In most cases, the bear is not so alert and not so near the den entrance. Usually, John must squeeze his broad-shouldered, six-foot-tall frame inside the den, and then,

Depressed and in pain from the accident, John returned to the University of Montana. By chance he overheard a conversation about a bear research project in Alaska. "The next thing I knew," he said, "I was on a small plane flying out over the flat, featureless snow of the north slope to some isolated field camp in the middle of nowhere. It was quite a contrast to the African tropics. I thought I had made a terrible mistake." But after one arctic summer following a radio-collared brown bear and her cubs across the tundra, John knew he had found his calling. –S. Q.

without room to **maneuver**, jab the tranquilizing needle into the waking bear.

Most people probably wouldn't want this job. But John feels that the chance to climb into the private world of a black bear is a great privilege. After studying North American bears for 20 years, John sees bears differently than most people do. "Bears are not vicious animals to be feared," he says. "I see a lot of the same traits in bears that I see in dogs, and even people including curiosity and playfulness. Sure, bears sometimes attack, but in nearly all cases there are specific circumstances that explain the bear's behavior. How would you feel if you were sleeping and woke up to see a stranger standing in the room? It's understandable if a surprised bear gets a bit upset."

maneuver to move in a planned position or direction

Too Close Encounters

You'd think John would have plenty of frightening bear stories. But he doesn't. "More bears are killed by people each year than vice-versa," he says. "I go out of my way not to have problems. I guess maybe I have had a lot of incidents that people who don't know bears might think were scary. But really it wasn't until last summer that I got into serious trouble. I surprised a brown bear with two yearlings in Katmai National Park. The sow charged. And she meant business."

Surprisingly, John is glad this happened. "Until then I couldn't be absolutely sure of what I would be capable of in that situation. I sort of wondered if I might just fall to the ground and start

John's main worry in his work is not his own safety, but that of the bears. "I enjoy the opportunity to study and handle bears," he says. "But I also hate to **hassle** them. It's important to me to be sure the work we are doing is worth what we are putting the bears through....But I have learned that we can't just leave bears alone and expect everything to be OK. We have to know more about bears and bear behavior to protect them and their habitats." ❖

....

hassle to cause trouble or annoy

Susan Quinlan writes to share her fascination with nature and biology. She is the author of two award-winning books: The Case of the Mummified Pigs *and* Other Mysteries in Nature and Puffins.

whimpering. But I used my knowledge of bear behavior. I faced the sow, talked softly, and backed away." Nobody got hurt—not John, not the bear.

One of John's projects is making a video on how to avoid trouble with bears—and what to do if you have a bear encounter. "Bears don't mind living with people," he says. "But whether or not bears survive in the future depends upon whether or not people can learn to live with bears." –S. Q.

Mythology

Perseus and the Quest for Medusa's Head

adapted from Old Greek Stories
by James Baldwin

I. The King's Cruel Challenge

Long ago in Greece, there lived a proud and daring young man named Perseus. His bold ways earned him the love of his fellows but also the anger of the king. The king of the land was both jealous and cruel, and soon he could think of nothing but how to shame Perseus and be rid of him forever.

One day, the king called all the noble young men of his country together and told them that he was soon to marry a queen from beyond the sea. He asked each of them to bring him a present to be given to the bride's father, for in those times it was the custom that when any man was to be married, he must offer costly gifts to the father of the bride.

"What kind of presents do you want?" said the young men.

"Horses," answered the king, for he knew that Perseus himself had no horses to give.

Perseus was **vexed** by the king's request, which he knew was meant to shame him. **Impulsively** he cried out, "Horses—is that all you ask? Why don't you ask for something worth having? Why don't you ask for Medusa's head?"

Upon hearing this, the king smiled **triumphantly**. "Then Medusa's head it shall be!" he said. "These young men may give me horses, but you, Perseus, must bring me the head of Medusa."

"And so I will," said Perseus **grimly**, and he went away in anger, while his young friends laughed at him because of his foolish words.

What was this Medusa's head which Perseus had so **rashly** promised to bring?

Far, far away, on the very edge of the world, said the Greeks, there lived three strange monsters, sisters called Gorgons. They had the bodies and faces of women, but they had wings of gold, terrible claws of brass, and hair that was full of living serpents. They were so awful to look upon that any man who saw their faces was turned to stone. Two of these monsters had charmed lives, and no weapon could ever do them harm, but the third, whose

....

vexed annoyed; distressed
impulsively without thinking ahead
triumphantly in the manner of celebrating some victory
grimly with stern determination
rashly thoughtlessly; hastily

name was Medusa, might be killed, if indeed anyone could find her and give her the fatal stroke.

When Perseus went away from the king's palace, he began to feel sorry that he had spoken so rashly. He walked down to the sea, wondering, "How will I ever make good my promise and meet the king's challenge? I do not know which way to go to find the Gorgons, and I have no weapon with which to slay the terrible Medusa. Still, I will never show my face to the king again, unless I bring the monster's head with me."

As Perseus thought, the sun went down and the moon arose and a soft wind came blowing from the west. Then, all at once, a man and a woman stood before him. Both were tall and noble. The man looked like a prince. There were wings on his cap and sandals, and he carried a winged staff, around which two golden serpents were twined.

"What is the matter, Perseus?" he asked, and Perseus told him how the king had treated him, and about the rash words he had spoken.

The lady replied, "Do not fear. Go out boldly in quest of the Gorgons, and we will help you obtain Medusa's terrible head." And as she spoke, Perseus noticed that although she was not beautiful, she had most wonderful gray eyes, a stern but lovable face, and a queenly form.

"But I have no horses and no ship. How will I get there?" said Perseus.

"You shall don my winged sandals," said the strange prince, "and they will bear you over sea and land."

"But how will I know where to go?" asked Perseus.

"I will tell you," said the queenly lady. "You must go first to the three Gray Sisters, who live beyond the frozen sea in the far, far north. They alone know where to find the maidens who guard the golden apples of the Western Land. The maidens will give you what you need to kill Medusa, and they will tell you how to reach the edge of the world where lies the home of the Gorgons."

Then the man took off his winged sandals, and put them on Perseus's feet, and the queenly lady whispered, "Be off at once, Perseus. Be bold and true, and fear nothing."

And Perseus knew that she was none other than Athena, the queen of the air, and that her companion was Hermes, the prince of the summer clouds. But before he could thank them for their kindness, they vanished in the dusky twilight.

II. The Gray Sisters

Perseus strapped on Hermes's winged sandals and leaped into the air. Swifter than an eagle, he flew through the sky, as the sandals carried him north over the sea, over cities and towns, over ranges of snowy mountains, and at last to the sea of ice. On he flew, among toppling icebergs, over frozen **billows**, and through air that the sun never warmed, until at last he came to the mouth of the cavern where the three Gray Sisters lived.

These three creatures were so old that they had forgotten their own age, and nobody could count how many years they had lived. Their long hair had been gray since they were born, and they had among them only a single eye and a single tooth, which they passed back and forth. Perseus heard them mumbling and **crooning** in their **dreary** home, and he listened.

"We know a secret which even the Great Folk who live on the mountaintop can never learn, don't we, sisters?" said one.

"Ha ha! That we do, that we do!" chattered the others. "We will never tell, never tell our secret. Not to man, not even to the Great Folk on the mountain!"

"Oh, we are clever! Give me the tooth, sister, that I may feel young and handsome again, too," said the one nearest to Perseus.

"And give me the eye that I may look out and see what is going on in the busy world," said the sister who sat next to her.

"Yes, yes," mumbled the third. And she took the tooth and the eye and reached them blindly toward the others.

....

billows waves
crooning speaking softly and gently
dreary cheerless; gloomy

Then, quick as thought, Perseus leaped forward and snatched both of the precious things from her hand.

"Where is the tooth? Where is the eye?" screamed the two, reaching out their long arms and **groping** here and there. "Have you dropped them, sister? Have you lost them?"

"I have your tooth and your eye," said Perseus, "and I will not give them back until you tell me your secret. Where are the maidens who keep the golden apples of the Western Land? Tell me how to find them!"

"Ah, sisters, we must tell him," whined one.

"Yes, we must tell him," moaned the others. "We must part with the secret to save our tooth and our eye."

So they told him how to reach the Western Land, and what road to follow to find the maidens who kept the golden apples. When they had made everything plain to him, Perseus gave them back their eye and tooth.

"Ha!" they laughed, "now the golden days of youth have come again!" And from that day to this, no man has ever seen the three Gray Sisters, nor does anyone know what became of them. The winds still whistle through their cheerless cave, the cold waves murmur on the shore of the wintry sea, and the ice mountains topple and crash, but no sound of living creature has since been heard in all that **desolate** land.

....

groping searching blindly
desolate bare; lifeless

PERSEUS AND THE QUEST FOR MEDUSA'S HEAD

III. The Maidens of the Western Land

Perseus left the cave of the Gray Sisters and leaped into the air. The winged sandals bore him south with the speed of the wind. Very soon he left the frozen sea behind him and came to a sunny land with tall forests, green meadows and valleys, and at last a pleasant garden **teeming** with all kinds of flowers and fruits.

The young man knew that this was the famous Western Land, for the Gray Sisters had told him what he should see there. He walked among the trees until he came to the center of the garden. There he came upon the three maidens singing and dancing around a tree heavy with golden apples. The wonderful tree with its precious fruit belonged to Hera, queen of earth and sky, and it was the maidens' duty to care for it and see that no one touched the golden apples.

Perseus stopped and listened to their song:

We sing of the old, we sing of the new—
Our joys are many, our sorrows are few;
Singing, dancing,
All hearts entrancing,
We wait to welcome the good and the true.

---

teeming abounding; filled to overflowing

The daylight is waning, the evening is here,
The sun will soon set, the stars will appear.
Singing, dancing,
All hearts entrancing,
We wait for the dawn of a glad new year.

The tree shall wither, the apples shall fall,
Sorrow shall come, and death shall call,
Alarming, grieving,
All hearts deceiving,
But hope shall abide to comfort us all.

Soon the tale shall be told, the song shall be sung,
The bow shall be broken, the harp unstrung,
Alarming, grieving,
All hearts deceiving,
Till every joy to the winds shall be flung.

But a new tree shall spring from the roots of the old,
And many a blossom its leaves shall unfold,
Cheering, gladdening,
With joy maddening,
*For its boughs shall be **laden** with apples of gold.*

Then Perseus went forward and spoke to the maidens.
They stopped singing, and stood still as if in alarm. But

---

laden heavily filled

when they saw the winged sandals on his feet, they ran to him, and welcomed him to the Western Land and to their garden.

"We knew that you were coming," they said, "for the winds told us. But why have you come?"

"I am on a quest to slay the monster Medusa," he said. "I have come to ask your help. Tell me, fair maidens, where I may find the monster's lair, and with what weapon I might slay it."

"We will do better than tell you," laughed the maidens, and the first came forward and buckled to Perseus's side a sword made of **adamant**. The second gave him a shield polished as brightly as a mirror. The third gave him a pouch that she hung by a long strap over his shoulder.

"With these three things, you will be able to slay the monster," said the maidens. "But here is a fourth, for without it, your quest will be **in vain**." And they gave him the Cap of Darkness, and when they had put it upon his head, not a creature on the earth or in the sky, not even the maidens themselves, could see him.

Then they told him where he would find the Gorgons, and what he should do to obtain the terrible head and escape alive. They wished him good luck, and bade him **hasten** to do the dangerous deed. So Perseus donned the

adamant a stone, like a diamond, once believed to be unbreakable
in vain useless
hasten to hurry

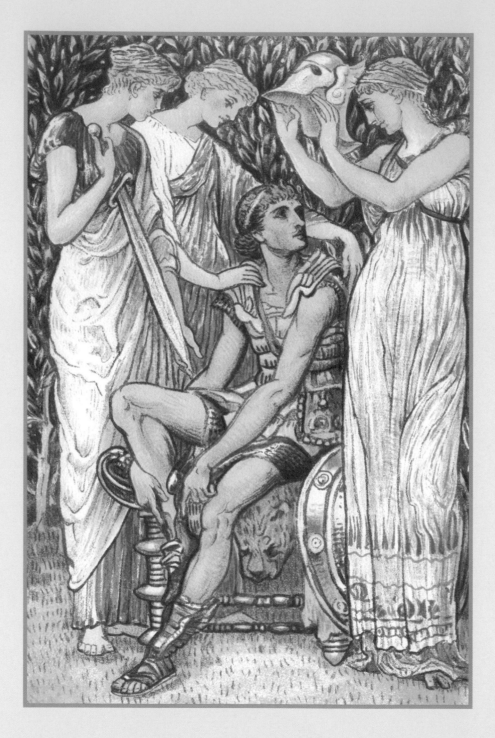

Cap of Darkness and sped away and away toward the edge of the earth, while the three maidens went back to their tree to sing and to dance and to guard the golden apples until the old world should become young again.

IV. The Dreadful Gorgons

With the keen-edged sword at his side and the bright shield upon his arm, Perseus flew bravely in search of the dreadful Gorgons. Because he also wore the Cap of Darkness, you could no more have seen him than you can see the wind. He flew so swiftly that it was not long until he had crossed the ocean and come to the sunless land where the lair of the Gorgons lay.

He heard a sound as of someone breathing heavily, and he looked around to see where it came from. Among the foul weeds growing close to the bank of a muddy river, something glittered in the pale light. He flew a little nearer, but he did not dare to look straight forward, lest he should all at once meet the gaze of a Gorgon and be turned to stone. So he flew backwards, and used the shining shield like a mirror to see the objects behind him.

And what a dreadful sight it was! Half hidden among the weeds lay the three monsters, fast asleep, with their golden wings folded about them. Their **brazen** claws were

....

brazen made of brass, or having the color of polished brass

stretched out as though ready to seize their prey, and their heads and shoulders were covered with sleeping snakes. The two largest of the Gorgons lay with their heads tucked under their wings, as birds hide their heads when they go to sleep. But the third, which lay between them, slept with her face turned up toward the sky, and Perseus knew that she was Medusa.

Very stealthily he went nearer and nearer, always with his back toward the monsters and always looking into his bright shield to see where to go. Then he drew his sword, and dashing quickly downward, struck a blow so sure and swift that the head of Medusa was cut from her shoulders. Without looking, he thrust the terrible head into his pouch and leaped again into the air, flying away with the speed of the wind.

Then the two older Gorgons awoke and rose with dreadful screams, and spread their great wings and dashed after him. They could not see him, for the Cap of Darkness hid him even from their eyes. But they scented the blood of the head that he carried in his pouch, and like hounds in the chase, they followed him, sniffing the air.

As he flew though the clouds, he could hear their dreadful cries and the clatter of their golden wings and the snapping of their horrible jaws. But Hermes's winged sandals were faster than any monster's wings. In a little while, the cries of the Gorgons were heard no more, and Perseus flew on alone.

V. The Great Sea Beast

Again Perseus crossed the great ocean and flew east until he came to a country where there were palm trees and pyramids and a great river flowing from the south. Here, as he looked down, a strange sight met his eyes. He saw a beautiful girl chained to a rock by the seashore, and far away, a huge sea beast swimming toward her to **devour** her. Without the least hesitation, he flew down and took off the Cap of Darkness.

"Oh, help me!" cried the girl when she saw the young hero, and she reached out her arms toward him.

Perseus drew his sword and cut the chain that held her, and then lifted her high upon the rock. But by this time, the sea monster was close at hand. It **lashed** the water with its tail and opened its wide jaws as though it would swallow not only Perseus and the young girl, but even the rock on which they were standing.

"Close your eyes!" Perseus cried to the girl. Then he swiftly pulled the head of Medusa from his pouch and held it up. The moment the monster saw the dreadful face, it stopped short and was turned to stone. And men say that the stone beast may be seen in that same spot to this day.

---

devour to eat greedily
lashed whipped

Then Perseus slipped the Gorgon's head back into the pouch, turned to the girl, and asked, "What is your name? And why are you here?"

"My name is Andromeda," the girl replied. "I am the daughter of the king of this land. My mother, the queen, was very beautiful and very proud of her beauty. Every day she came down to the seashore to look at her face in the water, and she boasted that not even the nymphs who live in the sea were as beautiful as she. When the sea nymphs heard this, they were very angry and asked Poseidon, the king of the sea, to punish my mother for her pride. So Poseidon sent the sea monster to crush our ships and kill the cattle along the shore and break down all the fishermen's huts.

"At last, my father was so distressed that he sent to Delphi to ask the **oracle** what he should do. And the oracle said that there was only one way to save the kingdom— that they must give me to the sea monster to be devoured.

"For a long time, my mother and father refused to do as the oracle said. But day after day, the monster laid waste to our land, and threatened to destroy not only the farms, but the towns as well. So I was chained to this rock and left to perish in the jaws of that awful beast."

As Andromeda told her story, the king and the queen, along with a great company of people, came down the

....

oracle in mythology, a being who was believed to have knowledge from the gods

shore, weeping and tearing their hair, for they were sure that by this time the monster had devoured the lovely princess. But when they saw her alive and well, and learned that she had been saved by the brave young man who stood beside her, their great grief turned to even greater joy.

"I will give you anything you wish as a reward for saving my daughter," cried the king. "Anything."

Perseus reached out his hand to the lovely girl and said, "What I wish most is for Andromeda to be my wife."

The king laughed heartily at Perseus's boldness and happily agreed. So Perseus and Andromeda were married, and there was a great feast in the king's palace, and everybody was merry and glad.

VI. The Journey's End

The two young people lived happily for some time in the land of palms and pyramids, but Perseus had not forgotten the challenge of the king who had sent him in quest of Medusa's head. One fine summer day, he and Andromeda sailed in a beautiful ship to his own home, for the winged sandals could not carry both him and his bride through the air.

When they arrived, Perseus went straight to the king, held up the pouch, and cried, "I promised to bring you Medusa's head, and here it is!"

"Nonsense!" scoffed the king. "A boy like you could no more kill Medusa than a wild boar. Take your pig's head, boy, and go play somewhere else." And all the court laughed.

But Perseus's eyes flashed fire and he asked, "Wouldn't you like to see it? Or are you afraid of this pig's head?"

"Show us," growled the king, his brows knit together in anger.

To the lords and ladies of the court, Perseus called out, "I **charge** you, if you value your lives, turn away, for this sight is for the king's eyes only." And he spoke so sternly that no one dared to ignore his warning.

Then with one swift motion, just as the king was drawing his sword to strike, Perseus lifted the head of terror from the pouch. The king saw it and was turned into stone, just as he stood, with his sword uplifted and his face twisted with anger.

But the people of the land were glad when they learned what had happened, for no one loved the cruel king. They were glad, too, because Perseus had come home again and had brought with him his lovely wife, Andromeda. So, after the people had talked the matter over among themselves, they went to Perseus and asked him to be their king.

"I thank you," he said, "and I will gladly rule over you, but for one day only. Then I will give the kingdom to another, for other adventures await me upon other shores."

charge to command

For that one day, he ruled the land, but **on the morrow**, he gave the kingdom to a fisherman he had known from his youth, whose wisdom all admired and whose judgment everyone trusted. Then he went on board his ship with Andromeda, and sailed away across the sea. ❖

....

on the morrow the next day

The Adventures of Theseus

adapted from Old Greek Stories
by James Baldwin

I. Sword and Sandals

Once, long ago, there lived a tall, **ruddy**-cheeked lad named Theseus. On the day Theseus turned fifteen years old, he went with his mother to the top of a mountain and looked out with her over the sea.

"Ah, if only your father would come!" she sighed.

"My father?" said Theseus, "Who is my father, and why are you always watching and waiting and wishing that he would come? Tell me about him."

She answered, "My child, do you see the great flat stone lying there under that tree, half buried in the ground, covered with moss and trailing ivy? Do you think you can lift it?"

"I do not know, but I will surely try," said Theseus. And he dug his fingers into the ground beside it, grasped its uneven edges, and tugged and strained until his breath came hard and his arms ached and his body was covered with sweat. Still, the stone would not budge. At last he said, "The task is too hard for me until I have grown stronger. But why do you wish me to lift it?"

....

ruddy healthy red

"When you are strong enough to lift it," she answered, "I will tell you about your father."

After that, the boy went out every day and practiced running and leaping and throwing and lifting, and every day he rolled some stone out of its place. At first he could move only a little weight, and those who saw him laughed as he pulled and puffed and grew red in the face, but never gave up until he had lifted it. And little by little he grew stronger, and his muscles became like iron bands.

On his next birthday, he went again up the mountain with his mother, and again tried to lift the great stone. But it remained fast in its place and was not moved.

"I am not yet strong enough, mother," he said.

"Have patience, my son," she replied.

So Theseus went on with his running and leaping and throwing and lifting. He practiced wrestling also, and tamed the wild horses of the plain, and hunted the lions among the mountains. His strength and swiftness and skill were the wonder of all men, and the land was filled with tales of his deeds.

Yet when Theseus tried again on his seventeenth birthday, he still could not move the great flat stone on the mountainside.

"Have patience, my son," his mother said, but this time there were tears in her eyes.

So Theseus went back again to his exercising, and he learned to **wield** a sword and a battle-ax, and to throw tremendous weights, and to carry great burdens. And men said that since the days of Hercules there was never such great strength in one body.

Then on the day he turned eighteen, Theseus climbed the mountain yet again with his mother. He stooped and took hold of the stone, and it yielded to his touch. When he had lifted it quite out of the ground, he found underneath it a sword of bronze and sandals of gold, and these he gave to her.

"Tell me now about my father," he said.

She said, "My son, your father is Aegeus, king of Athens. He himself lifted the great stone and laid the sword and sandals beneath it. Strong as he is, at his court also live your fifty cousins, who wish to be king when he dies, so he bade us stay here, far from any harm that they might do you. When you were but a babe, your father, the king, said that when you grew strong enough to lift the great stone, then you must take the sword and sandals and go seek him in Athens."

Then she buckled the sword to his belt and fastened the sandals upon his feet. Theseus's proud eyes flashed with eagerness, and he said, "I am ready, mother, and I will set out for Athens this very day."

....

wield to handle with skill

Then they walked down the mountain together and told Theseus's grandfather what had happened, and showed him the sword and the sandals. But the old man shook his head sadly and tried to **dissuade** Theseus from going.

"How can you go to Athens in these lawless times?" he said. "The sea is full of pirates. In fact, no ship from this land has sailed across the sea since your kingly father went home to his people, eighteen years ago."

Then, finding that this only made Theseus the more determined, he said, "If you must go, I will have a new ship built for you, strong and fast, and fifty of the bravest young men in the kingdom shall go with you. Perhaps, with fair winds and fearless hearts, you will escape the pirates and reach Athens in safety."

"Which is the most dangerous way?" asked Theseus. "To sail a ship across the sea or to make the journey on foot along the coast?"

"The sea is full enough of dangers," said his grandfather, "but the land route is **riddled** with dangers much greater. Even if there were good roads and no **obstacles**, the journey along the coast is a long one and would require many days. But there are also rugged mountains to climb, wide marshes to cross, and dark forests to go through. There is hardly a footpath in all that wild

....

dissuade to advise not to do something
riddled spread throughout
obstacles challenges; things that get in the way

region, nor any place to find rest or shelter. They say the woods are full of wild beasts, dreadful dragons lurk in the marshes, and many cruel robber giants dwell in the mountains."

"Well," said Theseus, "if there are more dangers by land than by sea, then I will go by land, and I go at once."

"But you will at least take fifty young men as companions with you?" asked his grandfather.

"No," said Theseus. "I go alone."

Then he kissed his mother and bade his grandfather good-bye, and left his home for the trackless coastland that lay to the west and north. With blessings and tears, his mother and grandfather followed him to the city gates, and watched him until his tall form was lost to sight among the trees that bordered the shore of the sea.

II. The Bed of Procrustes

With a brave heart, Theseus walked on, keeping the sea always upon his right. Soon he left behind the old city that was his home, and came to the great marshes, where the ground sank under him at every step, and green pools of **stagnant** water lay on both sides of the narrow path. No fiery dragon came out of the reeds to meet him, so

....

stagnant stale; still; unmoving

he walked on and on until he came to the rugged mountain land.

For days he kept up a steady pace, till Athens was not more than twenty miles away. But now the road was only a narrow path winding among the rocks and up and down many a lonely wooded **glen**. Theseus had seen worse and more dangerous roads than this, and so he strode onward, happy in the thought that he was near the end of his long journey. But it was very slow traveling among the mountains, and he was not always sure that he was following the right path.

The sun was almost down when he came to a broad green valley where the trees had been cleared away. A little river flowed through the middle of this valley, and on either side were grassy meadows where cattle were grazing, and on a hillside close by, half hidden among the trees, there was a great stone house with vines running over its walls and roof.

While Theseus was wondering who it could be that lived in this pretty but lonely place, a man came out of the house and hurried down to the road to meet him. He was a well-dressed man, and his face was **wreathed** with smiles, and he bowed low to Theseus and invited him kindly to come up to the house and be his guest that night.

....

glen a small valley
wreathed circled

"This is a lonely place," he said, "and it is not often that travelers pass this way. But there is nothing that gives me so much joy as to find strangers and feast them at my table and hear them tell of the things they have seen and heard. Come, good sir, and **sup** with me, and lodge under my roof, and you shall sleep on a wonderful bed which I have—a bed that fits every guest and cures him of every ill.

Theseus was pleased with the man's ways, and as he was both hungry and tired, he went up with him and sat down under the vines by the door. "Now," said the man, "I will go in and make the bed ready for you, and you can lie down upon it and rest. Later, when you feel refreshed, you shall sit at my table and sup with me, and I will listen to the pleasant tales I know you will tell."

When he had gone into the house, Theseus looked around him to see what sort of a place it was. He was filled with surprise at the richness of it—at the gold and silver and beautiful things with which every room seemed to be adorned—for it was indeed a place fit for a prince. While he was looking and wondering, the vines before him parted and the fair face of a young girl peeped out.

"Noble stranger," she whispered, "do not lie down on my master's bed, for those who do so never rise again. Fly down the glen and hide yourself in the deep woods before he returns, or else there will be no escape for you."

....

sup to eat supper; to dine

"Who is your master, fair maiden, that I should be afraid of him?" asked Theseus.

"Men call him Procrustes, or the Stretcher," said the girl, and she talked low and fast. "He is a robber. He brings **hither** all the strangers that he finds traveling through the mountains. He puts them on his iron bed, and robs them of all they have. No one who comes into his house ever goes out again."

"Why do they call him the Stretcher? And what is this iron bed of his?" asked Theseus.

"Did he not tell you that it fits all guests?" whispered the girl. "Most truly, it does fit them. For if a traveler is too long, Procrustes **hews** off his legs until he is the right length, but if he is too short, as is the case with most guests, then the terrible bed stretches the poor traveler's limbs and body until he is long enough. That is why men call him the Stretcher. But hark! I hear him coming!" As the girl quickly withdrew, the vine leaves closed over her hiding-place.

The next moment, Procrustes stood in the door, bowing and smiling as though he had never done any harm to his fellow men. "My dear young friend," he said, "the bed is ready, and I will show you the way. After you have taken a pleasant little nap, we will sit down at table and you may tell me of the wonderful things you have seen in the course of your travels."

---

hither here
hews cuts

Theseus arose and followed his host, and when they had come into an inner chamber, there, surely enough, was the bed. The frame was made of iron, very curiously **wrought**, and upon it a soft mattress seemed to invite him to lie down and rest. But Theseus, peering about, saw the ax and the ropes with **cunning** pulleys lying hidden behind the curtains.

"Now, my dear young friend," said Procrustes, "I pray you lie down and take your ease, for I know that you have traveled far and are faint from want of rest. Lie down, and while sweet slumber overtakes you, I will take care that no disturbing noise, nor buzzing fly, nor **vexing** gnat disturbs your dreams."

"Is this your wonderful bed?" asked Theseus.

"It is," answered Procrustes, "and you need but to lie down upon it, and it will fit you perfectly."

"But you must lie upon it first," said Theseus, "and let me see how it will fit itself to your **stature**."

"Ah no," said Procrustes, "for then the spell would be broken," and as he spoke, his cheeks grew ashy pale.

"But I tell you, you must lie upon it," said Theseus, and he seized the man around the waist and threw him by force upon the bed. And no sooner was he prone upon the couch

....

wrought made
cunning clever; crafty; tricky
vexing annoying
stature height

than curious iron arms reached out and clasped his body and held him so that he could not move hand or foot. The wretched man shrieked and cried for mercy, but Theseus stood over him and looked him straight in the eye.

"Is this the kind of hospitality you offer all your guests?" he asked.

Procrustes answered not a word. "Is it true," said Theseus, "that you have lured hundreds of travelers into your den only to rob them and make them fit your iron bed? Tell me, is this the awful truth?"

"It is true! It is true!" sobbed Procrustes, "and now kindly touch the spring above my head and let me go, and you shall have everything that I possess."

But Theseus turned away. "You are caught," he said, "in the trap you set for others and for me. Should there be mercy for the man who shows no mercy?" And Theseus went out of the room, and left Procrustes to the mercy of the terrible device.

Theseus looked through the house and found gold, silver, and many costly things that Procrustes had taken from the strangers who had fallen into his hands. He went into the dining hall, and there indeed was the table spread with a rich feast of meats and drinks and **delicacies** such as no king would scorn, but there was a seat and a plate for only the host, and none at all for guests.

....

delicacies rare and delicious treats

Then the girl whose fair face Theseus had seen among the vines came running into the house. She seized the young hero's hands and thanked him warmly.

"Only a month ago," she cried, "my father, a rich merchant of Athens, was traveling, and I was with him, happy and carefree as any bird in the green woods. This robber lured us into his den, for we had much gold with us. My father, he stretched upon his iron bed, but me he made his slave."

Then Theseus called together all the people in the house, poor wretches whom Procrustes had forced to serve him, and he divided the robber's **spoils** among them and told them they were free to go wherever they wished.

In the morning, Theseus went on, through the narrow crooked ways among the mountains and hills. At last, he came to the plain of Athens, and gazed out over the noble city. And in its midst, he saw the white walls of the palace of the king.

III. Honor and Home

As Theseus walked up the main street of the city, everyone wondered who the tall, fair youth could be. He continued straight to his father's palace.

"Where is the king?" he asked the guard.

....

spoils stolen items

"You cannot see the king," the guard answered, but, impressed by the noble bearing of the youth, he continued, "I will take you to his nephews."

The guard led the way into the feast hall, and there Theseus saw his fifty cousins sitting about the table, **swilling** ale, arguing, and making great fools of themselves. As Theseus stood in the doorway, his teeth clenched in anger, one of the feasters saw him and cried out, "Well, tall stranger, what do you want here?"

Theseus only replied, "I am here to ask that hospitality which men should never refuse to give."

"Nor do we refuse," cried they. "Come in! Eat, drink, and be our guest."

"I will come in," said Theseus, "but I will be the guest of the king. Where is he?"

"Never mind the king," said one of the feasters. "Anyway, we hold the real power—if you want to get anything done here, you have to go through us."

Barely able to restrain his anger, Theseus strode boldly past the **revelers** and into the main halls of the palace, searching for the king. At last he found Aegeus, lonely and sad, sitting in an inner chamber. Theseus's heart broke to see the lines of care and worry upon the old man's face.

---

swilling drinking greedily
revelers persons engaged in noisy partying

"Great king," he said gently, "I am a stranger in Athens and I have come to you to ask food and shelter and friendship such as I know you never deny."

"And who are you?" said the king.

"I am Theseus," answered the young man.

The king started and turned very pale—could this be the son whom he had so long hoped to see? His hands trembled as he felt his heart yearn strangely toward the young man. Then, checking himself, he said, "Yes! Yes! You are welcome, young hero, to such shelter and food and friendship as the King of Athens can give."

So, when the hour came, Theseus sat down to dine with the king, and while he ate he told of his deeds. He paused for a moment in his talk to help himself to a piece of the roasted meat, and as was the custom of the time, drew his sword to carve it. As the sword flashed from its scabbard, Aegeus saw the letters engraved upon it—the initials of his name. And he knew at once that it was the sword he had hidden so many years before under the stone on the mountainside by the city beyond the sea.

"My son! My son!" he cried, and he sprang up and flung his arms around Theseus. It was indeed a glad meeting for both father and son, and they had many things to ask and to tell.

The very next morning, Aegeus sent out his heralds to make it known all through the city that his son Theseus had arrived, and that he would in time be king **in his stead**. When the fifty nephews heard this, they were angry and alarmed.

"Shall this **upstart** cheat us out of our **heritage**?" they cried, and they made a plot to ambush Theseus in a grove close by the city gate.

Very cunningly did the wicked fellows lay their trap to catch the young hero. One morning, as he was passing that way alone, several of them fell suddenly upon him with swords and lances, and tried to slay him outright. They were thirty to one, but he faced them boldly and held them at bay, while he shouted for help. The men of Athens, who had borne so many wrongs at the hands of the greedy nephews, came running out from the streets. In the fight that followed, every one of the plotters was slain, and the other nephews, when they heard about it, fled from the city and never returned.

IV. The Black-Sailed Ship

For months, all the people of Athens were glad, for brave Theseus had come to live among them, and they felt confident that when his time came to rule, he would rule

---

in his stead in his place
upstart a person who acts more important than he or she really is
heritage something that one inherits

them well. But when the springtime came again, the doors of all the houses were shut and no man went in or out, but all sat silent with pale cheeks. A black-sailed ship stood ominously in the harbor, and a **host** of rude soldiers from Crete appeared, parading in the streets, shouting, "Hear us, all Athenians! In three days, your **tribute** will be due and must be paid!"

"What is the meaning of all this?" cried Theseus to the king. "Why do all look so fearfully at the black-sailed ship in the harbor? And what right does a Cretan have to demand tribute in Athens?"

With tears in his eyes, King Aegeus took the young prince aside and said, "Shortly after you were born, King Minos of Crete made war on Athens. When I heard the news, I hid the sword and sandals underneath the great stone, and then returned here at once. It was then I learned that some of your nephews had killed King Minos's only son and then spread the story that I had done it. They hoped that Minos would kill me so that one of them might become king."

"A foul and wicked deed!" cried Theseus.

"Minos came with all his army to **avenge** the death of his son," Aegeus continued. "He laid waste to the land, set fire to our ships, and surrounded the city. We asked for

---

host a great many
tribute in this usage, payment from one nation to another
avenge to get revenge for; to get even for

peace. He agreed, but in return for not destroying our city, he demanded a terrible tribute. Each year, seven youths and seven maidens must board the black-sailed ship and journey from Athens to Crete. There they are given to the Minotaur, a monster half-man and half-bull, that roams in the Labyrinth, a maze of rooms and corridors beneath the city.

"It is better," Aegeus sobbed, "that a few should die, even in so terrible a way, than all should be destroyed. I can say no more."

"But I will say more!" cried Theseus. "Athens shall not pay tribute to Crete. I myself will go with these youths and maidens, and I will slay the Minotaur and **defy** King Minos himself upon his throne."

"Oh, do not be so rash!" said the king, "for no one who is thrust into the Labyrinth ever comes out again. Remember that you are the hope of Athens. Do not take this great risk upon yourself."

"You say that I am the hope of Athens," said Theseus. "How then can I do anything but go?" And he began at once to make himself ready.

Three days later, all the youths and maidens of the city were brought together in the marketplace, so that lots might be cast for those who were to be taken. Two vessels of brass were brought and set before King Aegeus and the herald who had come from Crete. Into one vessel they

---

defy to challenge or confront

placed as many glass beads as there were noble young men in the city, and into the other as many as there were maidens. All the beads were white except seven in each vessel, and those were as black as ebony.

Then every maiden, without looking, reached her hand into one of the vessels and drew forth a bead, and those who drew the black beads were taken away to the black-sailed ship. The young men drew lots in the same way, but when six black beads had been drawn, Theseus came forward and said, "Hold! Let no more beads be drawn. I will be the seventh youth to pay this tribute. Now let us go aboard the black-sailed ship and be off."

Then the people and King Aegeus went down to the shore to take leave of the young men and maidens, whom they had no hope of seeing again. And all but Theseus wept and were brokenhearted.

"Father," said Theseus to the king, "do not weep. I will return."

"I hope that you may," said the old king. "And if when this ship returns, I see a white sail spread above the black one, then I shall know that you are alive and well, but if I see only the black one, it will tell me that you have perished."

And now the vessel was loosed from its mooring, the north wind filled the sail, and the seven youths and seven maidens were borne away over the sea, toward the dreadful fate that awaited them on the isle of Crete.

V. The Princess and the Labyrinth

When the ship reached Crete, the young people were set ashore. A party of soldiers led them through the streets toward the prison where they were to stay until morning. They did not weep, but with pale faces and firm-set lips they walked between the rows of houses, and looked neither to the right nor to the left. The windows and doors were full of people who were eager to see them.

"What a pity that such brave young men should be food for the Minotaur," muttered some.

"Ah, how awful that maidens so fair should meet a fate so sad!" sighed others.

Then they passed by the palace gate, where stood King Minos and his daughter, Ariadne.

"Indeed, those are noble young fellows," said the king.

"Yes, too noble to feed to the **vile** Minotaur," said Ariadne.

"The nobler, the better," said the king grimly. "For not one of them can compare with your lost brother."

Ariadne said no more, but she thought that she had never seen anyone who looked so much like a hero as young Theseus. How brave he was, how proud his eye, how firm his step!

That night, Ariadne made a plan to set Theseus and his companions free. At the earliest peep of day she

vile foul; repulsive; horrible

arose, while everyone else was asleep. She ran out of the palace and hurried to the prison. Since she was the king's daughter, the jailer opened the door at her bidding and allowed her to go in.

There sat the seven youths and the seven maidens on the ground, but they had not lost hope. She took Theseus aside and thrust a sword into his hand.

"Take this sword," she whispered, "for only with it can you hope to slay the Minotaur. And here is a ball of silken thread. As soon as you go into the Labyrinth, fasten one end of the thread to the stone doorpost, and unwind it as

you go along. When you have slain the Minotaur, follow the thread and it will lead you back to the door. In the meantime, I will make sure that your ship is ready to sail. Then I will wait for you at the door of the Labyrinth."

"Thank you, princess," said Theseus. "If I live to return to Athens, then it is my wish that you will return with me and be my bride."

Ariadne clasped his hands and smiled, and then she hastened away.

As soon as the sun was up, the guards came to lead the young prisoners to the Labyrinth. They did not see the sword Theseus hid behind him, nor the ball of silk that he held in his closed hand and tied swiftly to the doorpost as they entered.

The guards led the youths and maidens a long way into the Labyrinth, turning here and there, back and forth, a thousand different times, until it seemed certain that they could never find their way out again. Then, by a secret passage that they alone knew, the guards went out and left them, as they had left many others before, to wander about until the Minotaur found them.

"Do not fear," said Theseus to his companions. "Stay close to me, and I will protect you." And under his breath he whispered, "Athena, help and guard me!"

Then he drew his sword and stood in the narrow hall before them. For hours they waited, hearing no sound, seeing no shadow. At last, late in the day, they heard a bellowing, low and faint and far away. They listened and soon heard it again, a little louder, and very fierce and dreadful.

"The monster approaches!" cried Theseus. "Now for the fight!"

Then he shouted so loudly that the walls of the Labyrinth answered back, and the sound was carried upward to the sky and outward to the rocks and cliffs of the mountains. The Minotaur heard him, and his bellowing grew louder and fiercer every moment.

Theseus ran forward to meet the beast. The Minotaur came into view, rushing down the passage. He was twice as tall as a man, and his head was like a bull's with huge horns, fiery eyes, and a mouth as large and sharp as a lion's. When he saw Theseus with the sword in his hand coming to meet him, he paused, for no one had ever faced him in that way before. Then he put his head down and rushed forward, roaring furiously. At the last second, Theseus leaped aside and made a sharp thrust with his sword into the monster's leg as he passed.

The Minotaur fell upon the ground, groaning and beating wildly about with his horned head and his hoof-like fists. Theseus ran up and thrust the sword into the creature's heart. He was away again before the beast could harm him, and soon the Minotaur turned his face to the sky and lay dead.

The youths and maidens ran to Theseus, weeping and thanking him, but Theseus only said, "Come, let us hurry. Follow me as I wind up the silken thread, and we will find our way out of this **gruesome** Labyrinth."

Through a thousand rooms and courts and winding ways they went. At midnight, they came at last to the outer door and saw the city lying in the moonlight before them. Only a little way off was the seashore where the

....

gruesome horrible, usually as the result of some terrible violence

black-sailed ship that had brought them to Crete was moored. There stood Ariadne, waiting for them.

"The wind is fair, and the sea is smooth," she whispered to Theseus as she took his arm.

When the morning dawned they were far out to sea, and looking back from the deck of the little vessel, only the white tops of the Cretan mountains were in sight. And when King Minos arose and found his daughter gone, he tore his hair and cried, "Now indeed, I am **bereft** of all my treasures."

In the meantime, King Aegeus of Athens stayed day after day on a high tower by the shore, hoping to see a ship coming from the south. At last, the vessel with Theseus and his companions came in sight. But it still carried only the black sail, for in their haste and joy, the young men had forgotten to raise the white one.

"Alas! Alas! My son has perished!" moaned Aegeus, and he fainted and fell forward into the sea and was drowned. Thus did sadness cast a shadow on the joy of the homecoming of Theseus and the Athenian youths and maidens.

Theseus became king of Athens. He ruled the city wisely and well. One of his first commands was to order that in the harbor a monument be built to the memory of his father. And that sea, even to this day, has been called by the name of the good old king, the Aegean Sea. ❖

....

bereft deprived or robbed

Atalanta, the Fleet-Footed Huntress

adapted from Old Greek Stories
by James Baldwin

I. The Bear on the Mountain

In a sunny land in Greece called Arcadia, there lived a king and a queen who had no children. They wanted very much to have a son who might live to rule over Arcadia when the king was dead. And after many years, a child was born to them, but it was a little girl.

"What is a girl good for?" raged the king. "She can never do anything but sing and spin. If the child had been a boy, he might have learned to do many things—to ride, to hunt, and to fight in the wars, and by and by, he would rule as king of Arcadia. But this girl can never be a king."

Then in his wild rage he called to one of his men and bade him take the babe out to a mountain where there was nothing but rocks and thick woods and leave it there. The man carried the child far up the mountainside and laid it down on a bed of moss in the shadow of a great rock. The child stretched out its baby hands toward him and smiled, but he turned away and left it there, for he did not dare to disobey the king.

For a whole night and a whole day the babe lay on its bed of moss, wailing for its mother, but only the birds among the trees heard its **pitiful** cries. At last it grew so weak for want of food that it could only moan and move its head a little from side to side.

Just before dark on the second evening, a she-bear came strolling down the mountainside from her den. She was looking for her cubs, for some hunters had stolen them that very day while she was away from home, and they were nowhere to be found.

As the stars came out, the she-bear heard the babe's moans and saw it lying helpless on its bed of moss. She looked at it kindly, licked its face with her warm tongue, and then lay down beside it, just as she would have done with her own little cubs. The babe was too young to feel afraid, and it cuddled close to the old bear and felt that it had found a friend. After a while it fell asleep, but the bear guarded it until morning and then went down the mountainside to look for food.

In the evening, the bear came again and carried the child to her own den under the shelter of a rock where vines and wild flowers grew, and every day after that she came and gave the child food and played with it. Soon, all the bears on the mountain learned about the wonderful cub and came to see it, and not one of them tried to harm it.

....

pitiful sad; deserving compassion

The little girl grew quickly and became strong. After a while, she could walk and run among the trees and rocks and brambles on the round top of the mountain; but her bear mother would not allow her to wander far from the den beneath the rock where the vines and the wild flowers grew.

One day, some hunters came up the mountain to look for game. One of them pulled aside the vines that grew in front of the old bear's home. He was surprised to see the beautiful child lying on the grass and playing with the flowers she had gathered. But at sight of him, she leaped to her feet and bounded away like a frightened deer. She led the hunters on a fine chase among the trees and rocks, but there were a dozen of them and by circling her they managed at last to catch her.

The child struggled and fought as hard as she knew how, but it was no use. The hunters carried her down the mountain, and took her to the house where they lived on the other side of the forest. At first she cried all the time, for she sadly missed the bear that had been a mother to her for so long. But the hunters were very kind and treated her like their daughter. And so, slowly, she also came to like her new home.

The hunters named the girl Atalanta. When she grew older, they made her a bow and arrows and taught her how to shoot, and they gave her a light spear and showed her how to carry it and how to hurl it at game or at an enemy.

They took her with them when they went hunting, and there was nothing in the world that pleased her so much as roaming through the woods and running after the deer and other wild animals. Her feet became very swift, so that she could run faster than any of the men. Her arms were so strong and her eyes so sharp that with her arrow or her spear she never missed the mark. And she grew up to be very tall and graceful, and was known throughout all Arcadia as Atalanta, the fleet-footed huntress.

II. The Wild Boar of Calydon

Not very far from the land of Arcadia there was a little city named Calydon. It lay in the midst of rich wheat fields and fruitful vineyards, but beyond the vineyards was a deep, **dense** forest where many wild beasts lived. One day, the largest and fiercest wild boar that anybody had ever seen came rushing out of the forest. It had two long tusks which stuck far out of its mouth on either side and were as sharp as knives, and the stiff bristles on its back were as long as knitting needles.

The wild boar raced towards Calydon, **champing** its teeth and foaming at the mouth. It rushed into the wheat fields and tore up all the grain, it charged into the vineyard

---

dense thick
champing chewing loudly and impatiently; gnashing

and broke down all the vines, it rooted up all the trees in the orchards, and when there was nothing else to do, it **hurtled** into the pastures among the hills and killed the sheep that were feeding there.

The beast was so fierce and so swift that everyone fled before it. Its thick skin was proof against arrows and against such spears as the people of Calydon had, and many brave warriors who tried to attack the boar died at the edge of its terrible razor tusks. For weeks, it ran wild about the countryside, and the only safe place for anybody was inside the city walls.

At last, when it had laid waste to much of the country, the boar went back into the edge of the forest. But the people were so much afraid of it that they lived in constant dread that the beast should come again and tear down the gates of the city.

So the king of Calydon sent messengers into all the countries nearby, asking the bravest men and the most skillful hunters to come at a certain time and help him hunt and kill the great wild boar. When the day came, there was a wonderful gathering of men at Calydon. The greatest heroes in the world were there. Everyone was fully armed, and all expected to have fine sport hunting the terrible beast. With the warriors from the south came Atalanta, armed with bow and arrows and a long hunting spear.

....

hurtled rushed forcefully

"My daughters are having a game of ball in the garden," said the king to the huntress. "Would you like to put away your arrows and your spear and go play with them?"

Atalanta shook her head and lifted her chin in **disdain**.

"Perhaps you would rather stay with the queen, and look at the women spin and weave," said the king.

"No," answered Atalanta. "I am going with the warriors to hunt the wild boar in the forest."

The men gasped. They had never heard of such a thing as a girl going out with heroes to hunt wild boars.

"If she goes, then I will not," muttered one.

"Nor will I," said another, a little more loudly. "Why, the whole world would laugh at us, and we should never hear the end of it."

"Nor will I," exclaimed a third. "The hunt is for heroes, not for girls."

Many of the men **guffawed** and hooted at the young huntress. But Atalanta only grasped her spear more firmly and stood tall and straight in the gateway of the palace.

Just then, the youngest prince of Calydon came forward. His name was Meleager.

"What's this?" he cried. "Who says that Atalanta shall not go to the hunt? Why, I believe you are afraid that

....

disdain scorn; contempt
guffawed laughed loudly

she'll be braver than you. Fine heroes you are! Let all such cowards go home at once."

All laughter died away in a moment, and not a single man moved. And it was settled then and there that Atalanta would go with the heroes to hunt the wild boar, though some of the men kept muttering and complaining among themselves.

For nine days, the heroes and huntsmen feasted in the halls of the king of Calydon. Early on the tenth, they set out for the forest. Soon they came upon the great beast, which came charging out upon his foes.

The heroes hid behind the trees or climbed up among the branches, for they had not expected to see so terrible a creature. The boar stood in the middle of a glade, pawing the ground with his hooves, and tearing it up with his tusks. White foam rolled from his mouth, his eyes glistened like red fire, and he grunted so fiercely that the woods and hills echoed with fearful sounds.

One of the bravest of the men threw his spear, but that only made the beast fiercer than ever. He charged the warrior, caught him before he could scramble into a tree, and tore him to pieces in a mad fury. Another man leapt out from his hiding place and was also killed. Then one of the oldest and noblest of the heroes launched his spear with a mighty heave, but it only grazed the boar's tough skin and glanced away. The boar was getting the best of the fight.

Softly, Atalanta stepped out into the glade. She leveled her spear, and threw it with all her might. The boar squealed as the sharp point pierced its skin. It ran about in a **frenzy**, **heedless** of the hunters and their arrows and spears. Then Meleager rushed up and thrust his spear into its heart. The terrible creature thrashed and then rolled over, dead.

The heroes then cut off the boar's skin and offered it to Meleager as a prize, because he had given the boar its death wound.

....

frenzy wild, frantic activity
heedless paying no attention to; thoughtless

But Meleager said, "It belongs to Atalanta, because it was she who wounded the boar first." And he gave the skin to her as the prize of honor.

III. Atalanta's Race

After the hunt at Calydon, Atalanta went back to her old home among the mountains of Arcadia. She was still the fleet-footed huntress, and she was never so happy as when in the green woods wandering among the trees or chasing the wild deer. All the world had heard about her, however, and the young heroes in the lands nearest to Arcadia did nothing else but talk about her beauty, grace, swiftness, and courage.

Of course every one of these young fellows wanted her to become his wife, and she might have been a queen any day if she had only said the word, for the richest king in Greece would have been glad to marry her. But she cared nothing for any of the young men. She preferred the freedom of the green woods to all the **luxuries** she might have enjoyed in a palace.

But the young men would not take "No!" for an answer. They could not believe that she really meant it, so they kept coming and staying until the woods of Arcadia were full of them, and there was no getting along with them at all.

luxuries unnecessary comforts

So when she could think of no other way to get rid of them, Atalanta called them together and said, "You want to marry me, do you? Well, if any one of you would like to run a race with me from this mountain to the riverbank, he may do so. I will be the wife of the one who outruns me."

"Agreed! Agreed!" cried all the young fellows.

"But listen!" she said. "Whoever tries this race must also agree that if I outrun him, he must lose his life."

The men glanced **furtively** at one another. Many of them drew away from the crowd, melted into the trees, and turned their hurried footsteps towards home.

Those who stayed said, "We agree. But if we are to risk our lives, won't you at least give us a head start?"

"As you wish," she answered. "I will give you a start of a hundred paces. But remember, if I overtake anyone before he reaches the river, he shall lose his life that very day."

Several others now decided that they were not feeling well or that business called them home, so they also left the crowd. But a few who had some practice sprinting across the country stayed and made up their minds to try their luck. Could a mere girl outrun such fine fellows as they? Nonsense!

And so it happened that a race was run almost every day, and almost every day some poor fellow lost his life, for the swiftest sprinter in all Greece was overtaken by Atalanta long before he could reach the riverbank.

....

furtively furtively slyly; sneakily

Then one day there came from a distant land a fine young man named Hippomenes. Atalanta liked his kind expression and his **courteous** manner. She dearly hoped that this young man would not put himself to the test in a race against her.

"You had better not run with me," said Atalanta, "for I am sure to overtake you, and you will lose your life."

"Ah, my good lady, that remains to be seen," replied Hippomenes, with a curious twinkle in his eyes. For before he had come to try his chance, Hippomenes had sought the help of Aphrodite, the queen of love, who lived among the clouds on Mount Olympus. And Hippomenes was so gentle and wise and brave that Aphrodite took pity on him. She gave him three golden apples and told him how he might use them to defeat the fleet-footed huntress in a race.

On the day of the race, Atalanta tried again to persuade Hippomenes not to run, for she also took pity on him.

"I'm sure to overtake you," she said. "Please, don't lose your life needlessly."

"I won't," laughed Hippomenes, and away he sped. But in his pocket, he carried Aphrodite's three golden apples.

Atalanta gave him a good start and then she followed after, as swift as an arrow shot from the bow. Hippomenes was not a very fast runner, and it would not be hard for her to overtake him. She thought that she would let him get almost to the goal, for she really pitied him. But when

---

courteous polite; considerate

he heard her quick breath behind him, he threw one of the
golden apples over his shoulder.

As the apple fell to the ground, Atalanta saw how
beautiful it was, and she stopped to pick it up. While she
was doing this, Hippomenes gained a good many paces.
But in a minute she was as close behind him as ever.

And yet, she really did pity him.

Just then, Hippomenes threw the second apple over his
shoulder. It was handsomer and larger than the first, and
Atalanta could not bear the thought of allowing someone
else to get it. So she stopped to pick it up from where it
had fallen among the long grass. It took longer to find it

than she had expected, and when she looked up again, Hippomenes was a hundred feet ahead of her. But that was no matter; she could easily overtake him.

And yet, how she did pity the foolish young man!

Hippomenes heard her footsteps thundering just a few paces behind him. He took the third apple and threw it over to one side of the path where the ground sloped toward the river. Atalanta's quick eye saw that it was far more beautiful than either of the others. If it were not picked up at once, it would roll down into the deep water and be lost, and that would never do. She turned aside from her course and ran after it. It was easy enough to retrieve the apple, but while she was doing so, Hippomenes gained upon her again. He was almost to the riverbank. How she strained every muscle now to overtake him!

But after all, she felt that she did not care very much. He was the finest young man that she had ever seen, he had given her three golden apples, and he had risked his life to win her. It would be a great pity if he should have to die.

So she slowed her steps, and let him reach the riverbank first.

After that, Atalanta became Hippomenes's wife. And the young man took the fleet-footed huntress with him to his distant home, and there they lived happily together for many, many years. ❖

Friendship

Friendship needs no **studied** phrases,
  Polished face, or winning **wiles**;
Friendship deals no **lavish** praises,
  Friendship **dons** no surface smiles.

Friendship follows Nature's **diction**,
  Shuns the **blandishments** of art,
Boldly **severs** truth from fiction,
  Speaks the language of the heart.

Friendship favors no condition,
  Scorns a narrow-minded **creed**,
Lovingly fulfills its mission,
  Be it word or be it deed.

Friendship cheers the faint and weary,
  Makes the timid spirit brave,
Warns the **erring**, lights the dreary,
  Smooths the passage to the grave.

Friendship—pure, unselfish friendship,
  All through life's **allotted** span,
Nurtures, strengthens, widens, lengthens,
  Man's relationship with man. ❖

---

studied carefully made
wiles tricks
lavish excessive
dons puts on
diction way of speaking; use of words
shuns rejects

blandishments flattery; false praise
severs separates; cuts off
creed a set of beliefs
erring those who make mistakes
allotted a given portion
nurtures nourishes; develops

Damon and Pythias

dramatized for radio by Fan Kissen

Cast

DAMON	PYTHIAS
KING	FIRST VOICE
SECOND VOICE	THIRD VOICE
FIRST ROBBER	SECOND ROBBER
SOLDIER	MOTHER

(Sound: Iron door opens and shuts. Key in lock.)
(Music: Up full and out.)

NARRATOR: Long, long ago there lived on the island of Sicily two young men named Damon and Pythias. They were known far and wide for the strong friendship each had for the other. Their names have come down to our own times to mean true friendship. You may hear it said of two persons:

FIRST VOICE: Those two? Why, they're like Damon and Pythias!

NARRATOR: The king of that country was a cruel **tyrant**. He made cruel laws, and he showed no mercy toward anyone who broke his laws. Now, you might very well wonder.

SECOND VOICE: Why didn't the people rebel?

NARRATOR: Well, the people didn't dare rebel because they feared the king's great and powerful army. No one dared say a word against the king or his laws—except Damon and Pythias speaking against a new law the king had proclaimed.

SOLDIER: Ho, there! Who are you that dares to speak so about our king?

PYTHIAS: *(Unafraid)* I am called Pythias.

---

tyrant a ruler who uses power cruelly and unjustly

SOLDIER: Don't you know it is a crime to speak against the king or his laws? You are under arrest! Come and tell this opinion of yours to the king's face!

(Music: A few short bars in and out.)

NARRATOR: When Pythias was brought before the king, he showed no fear. He stood straight and quiet before the throne.

KING: *(Hard, cruel)* So, Pythias! They tell me you do not approve of the laws I make.

PYTHIAS: I am not alone, your majesty, in thinking your laws are cruel. But you rule the people with such an iron hand that they dare not complain.

KING: *(Angry)* But you have the daring to complain for them! Have they appointed you their champion?

PYTHIAS: No, your majesty. I speak for myself alone. I have no wish to make trouble for anyone. But I am not afraid to tell you that the people are suffering under your rule. They want to have a voice in making the laws for themselves. You do not allow them to speak up for themselves.

KING: In other words, you are calling me a tyrant! Well, you shall learn for yourself how a tyrant treats a rebel! Soldier! Throw this man into prison!

SOLDIER: At once, your majesty! Don't try to resist, Pythias!

PYTHIAS: I know better than to try to resist a soldier of the king! And for how long am I to remain in prison, your majesty, merely for speaking out for the people?

KING: *(Cruel)* Not for very long, Pythias. Two weeks from today at noon, you shall be put to death in the public square as an example to anyone else who may dare to question my laws or acts. Off to prison with him, soldier!

(Music: In briefly and out.)

NARRATOR: When Damon heard that his friend Pythias had been thrown into prison, and about the severe punishment that was to follow, he was heartbroken. He rushed to the prison and persuaded the guard to let him speak to his friend.

DAMON: Oh, Pythias! How terrible to find you here! I wish I could do something to save you!

PYTHIAS: Nothing can save me, Damon, my dear friend. I am prepared to die. But there is one thought that troubles me greatly.

DAMON: What is it? I will do anything to help you.

PYTHIAS: I'm worried about what will happen to my mother and my sister when I'm gone.

DAMON: I'll take care of them, Pythias, as if they were my own mother and sister.

PYTHIAS: Thank you, Damon. I have money to leave them. But there are other things I must arrange. If only I could go see them before I die! But they live two days' journey from here, you know.

DAMON: I'll go to the king and beg him to give you your freedom for a few days. You'll give your word to return at the end of that time. Everyone in Sicily knows you for a man who has never broken his word.

PYTHIAS: Do you believe for one moment that the king would let me leave this prison, no matter how good my word may have been all my life?

DAMON: I'll tell him that I shall take your place in the prison cell. I'll tell him that if you do not return by the appointed day, he may kill me in your place!

PYTHIAS: No, no, Damon! You must not do such a foolish thing! I cannot—I will not—let you do this! Damon! Damon! Don't go! *(To himself)* Damon, my friend! You may find yourself in a cell beside me!

(Music: In briefly and out.)

DAMON: *(Begging)* Your majesty! I beg of you! Let Pythias go home for a few days to bid farewell to his mother and sister. He gives his word that he will return at your appointed time. Everyone knows that his word can be trusted.

KING: In ordinary business affairs—perhaps. But he is now a man under sentence of death. To free him even for a few days would strain his honesty—any man's honesty—too far. Pythias would never return here! I consider him a **traitor**, but I'm certain he's no fool.

DAMON: Your majesty! I will take his place in the prison until he comes back. If he does not return, then you may take my life in his place.

KING: *(Astonished)* What did you say, Damon?

DAMON: I'm so certain of Pythias that I am offering to die in his place if he fails to return on time.

KING: I can't believe you mean it!

DAMON: I do mean it, your majesty.

KING: You make me very curious, Damon, so curious that I'm willing to put you and Pythias to the test. This exchange of prisoners will be made. But Pythias must be back two weeks from today, at noon.

DAMON: Thank you, your majesty!

KING: The order with my official seal shall go by your own hand, Damon. But I warn you, if your friend does not return on time, you shall surely die in his place! I shall show no mercy.

(Music: In briefly and out.)

NARRATOR: Pythias did not like the king's bargain with Damon. He did not like to leave his friend in prison with the chance that he might lose his life if something

traitor a person who betrays a cause or country

went wrong. But at last Damon persuaded him to leave and Pythias set out for his home. More than a week went by. The day set for the death sentence drew near. Pythias did not return. Everyone in the city knew of the condition on which the king had permitted Pythias to go home. Everywhere people met, the talk was sure to turn to the two friends.

FIRST VOICE: Do you suppose Pythias will come back?

SECOND VOICE: Why should he stick his head under the king's ax once he has escaped?

THIRD VOICE: Still, would an honorable man like Pythias let such a good friend die for him?

FIRST VOICE: There's no telling what a man will do when it's a question of his own life against another's.

SECOND VOICE: But if Pythias doesn't come back before the time is up, he will be killing his friend.

THIRD VOICE: Well, there's still a few days' time. I, for one, am certain that Pythias will return in time.

SECOND VOICE: And I am just as certain that he will not. Friendship is friendship, but a man's own life is something stronger, I say!

NARRATOR: Two days before the time was up, the king himself visited Damon in his prison cell.

(Sound: Iron door unlocked and opened.)

KING: *(Mocking)* You see now, Damon, that you were a fool to make this bargain. Your friend has tricked you! He will not come back here to be killed! He has **deserted** you.

DAMON: *(Calm and firm)* I have faith in my friend. I know he will return.

KING: *(Mocking)* We shall see!

(Sound: Iron door shut and locked.)

NARRATOR: Meanwhile, when Pythias reached the home of his family, he arranged his business affairs so that his mother and sister would be able to live comfortably for the rest of their years. Then he said a last farewell to them before starting back to the city.

MOTHER: *(In tears)* Pythias, it will take you two days to get back. Stay another day, I beg you!

PYTHIAS: I dare not stay longer, Mother. Remember, Damon is locked up in my prison cell while I'm gone. Please don't weep for me. My death may help bring better days for all our people.

NARRATOR: So Pythias began his journey in plenty of time. But bad luck struck him on the very first day. At twilight, as he walked along a lonely stretch of woodland, a rough voice called:

FIRST ROBBER: Not so fast there, young man! Stop!

PYTHIAS: *(Startled)* Oh! What is it? What do you want?

deserted left behind; abandoned

SECOND ROBBER: Your money bags.

PYTHIAS: My money bags? I have only this small bag of coins. I shall need them for some favors, perhaps, before I die.

FIRST ROBBER: What do you mean, before you die? We don't mean to kill you, only take your money.

PYTHIAS: I'll give you my money, only don't delay me any longer. I am to die by the king's order three days from now. If I don't return on time, my friend must die in my place.

FIRST ROBBER: A likely story! What man would be fool enough to go back to prison ready to die?

SECOND ROBBER: And what man would be fool enough to die for you?

FIRST ROBBER: We'll take your money, all right. And we'll tie you up while we get away.

PYTHIAS: *(Begging)* No! No! I must get back to free my friend! *(Fade)* I must go back!

NARRATOR: But the two robbers took Pythias's money, tied him to a tree, and went off as fast as they could. Pythias struggled to free himself. He cried out for a long time. But no one traveled through that lonesome woodland after dark. The sun had been up for many hours before he finally managed to free himself from the ropes that had tied him to the tree. He lay on the ground, hardly able to breathe.

(Music: In briefly and out.)

NARRATOR: After a while Pythias got to his feet. Weak and dizzy from hunger and thirst and his struggle to free himself, he set off again. Day and night he traveled without stopping, desperately trying to reach the city in time to save Damon's life.

(Music: Up and out.)

NARRATOR: On the last day, half an hour before noon, Damon's hands were tied behind his back, and he was taken into the public square. The people muttered angrily as Damon was led in by the jailer. Then the king entered and seated himself on a high platform.

(Sound: Crowd voices in and hold under single voices.)

SOLDIER: *(Loud)* Long live the king!

FIRST VOICE: *(Low)* The longer he lives, the more miserable our lives will be!

KING: *(Loud, mocking)* Well, Damon, your lifetime is nearly up. Where is your good friend Pythias now?

DAMON: *(Firm)* I have faith in my friend. If he has not returned, I'm certain it is through no fault of his own.

KING: *(Mocking)* The sun is almost overhead. The shadow is almost at the noon mark. And still your friend has not returned to give back your life!

DAMON: *(Quiet)* I am ready and happy to die in his place.

KING: *(Harsh)* And you shall, Damon! Jailer, lead the prisoner to the—

(Sound: Crowd voices up to a roar, then under.)

FIRST VOICE: *(Over noise)* Look! It's Pythias!

SECOND VOICE: *(Over noise)* Pythias has come back!

PYTHIAS: *(Breathless)* Let me through! Damon!

DAMON: Pythias!

PYTHIAS: Thank the gods I'm not too late!

DAMON: *(Quiet, sincere)* I would have died for you gladly, my friend.

CROWD VOICES: *(Loud, demanding)* Set them free! Set them both free!

KING: *(Loud)* People of the city! *(Crowd voices out.)* Never in all my life have I seen such faith and friendship, such loyalty between men. There are many among you who call me harsh and cruel. But I cannot kill any man who proves such strong and true friendship for another. Damon and Pythias, I set you both free. *(Roar of approval from crowd.)* I am king. I command a great army. I have stores of gold and precious jewels. But I would give all my money and power for one friend like Damon or Pythias.

(Sound: Roar of approval from crowd up briefly and out.)

(Music: Up and out.) ❖

The Birth-Time of the Gods

from Old-World Japan: Legends of the Land of the Gods
retold by Frank Rinder

Before time was, and while yet the world was uncreated, **chaos** reigned. The earth and the waters, the light and the darkness, the stars and the **firmament**, were intermingled in a vaporous liquid. All things were formless and confused. No creature existed; phantom shapes moved as clouds on the ruffled surface of a sea. It was the birth-time of the gods. The first deity sprang from an immense bulrush-bud, which rose, spear-like, in the midst of the boundless disorder. Other gods were born, but three generations passed before the actual separation of the atmosphere from the more solid earth. Finally, where the tip of the bulrush points upward, the Heavenly Spirits appeared.

From this time their kingdom was divided from the lower world where chaos still prevailed. To the fourth pair of gods it was given to create the earth. These two beings were the powerful God of the Air, Izanagi, and the fair Goddess of the Clouds, **Izanami**. From them sprang all life.

Now Izanagi and Izanami wandered on the Floating Bridge of Heaven. This bridge spanned the gulf between

chaos disorder, confusion
firmament the sky or heavens
Izanami ee-zah-nah-mee

heaven and the unformed world. It was upheld in the air, and it stood secure. The God of the Air spoke to the Goddess of the Clouds: "There must be a kingdom beneath us, let us visit it." Then he plunged his jeweled spear into the **seething** mass below. The drops that fell from the point of the spear thickened and became the island of Onogoro. Thereupon the Earth-Makers descended, and called up a high mountain peak, on whose summit could rest one end of the Heavenly Bridge, and around which the whole world should revolve.

The Wisdom of the Heavenly Spirit had commanded that Izanagi should be a man, and Izanami a woman. These two deities decided to wed and dwell together on the earth. But, as befitted their majestic birth, the wooing must be sincere. Izanagi skirted the base of the mountain to the right, Izanami turned to the left. When the Goddess of the Clouds saw the God of the Air approaching afar off, she cried, enraptured: "Ah, what a fair and lovely youth!" Then Izanagi exclaimed, "Ah, what a fair and lovely maiden!" As they met, they clasped hands, and the marriage was accomplished. But, for some unknown cause, the union did not prove as happy as the god and goddess had hoped. They continued their work of creation, but Awaji, the island that rose from the deep, was little more than a barren waste, and their first-born son, Hiruko, was a weakling.

....

seething agitated

The Earth-Makers placed him in a little boat woven of reeds and left him to the mercy of wind and tide.

In deep grief, Izanagi and Izanami returned across the Floating Bridge, and came to the place where the Heavenly Spirits hold eternal audience. From them they learned that Izanagi should have been the first to speak, when the gods met round the base of the Pillar of Earth. They must woo and wed anew. On their return to earth, Izanagi, as before, went to the right, and Izanami to the left of the mountain, but now, when they met, Izanagi exclaimed: "Ah, what a fair and lovely maiden!" and Izanami joyfully responded, "Ah, what a fair and lovely youth!" They clasped hands once more, and their happiness began. They created the eight large islands of the Kingdom of Japan; first the luxuriant Island of the Dragon-fly, the great Yamato; then Tsukushi, the White-Sun Youth; Iyo, the Lovely Princess, and many more. The rocky islets of the **archipelago** were formed by the foam of the rolling breakers as they dashed on the coast-lines of the islands already created. Thus, China and the remaining lands and continents of the world came into existence.

Now were born to Izanagi and Izanami, the Ruler of the Rivers, the Deity of the Mountains, and, later, the God of the Trees, and a goddess to whom was entrusted the care of tender plants and herbs.

....

archipelago a group of islands

Then Izanagi and Izanami said: "We have created the mighty Kingdom of the Eight Islands, with mountains, rivers, and trees; yet another divinity there must be, who shall guard and rule this fair world."

As they spoke, a daughter was born to them. Her beauty was dazzling. Her throne should be set high above the clouds as befit her regal bearing. She was none other than Ama-terasu, the Heaven-Illuminating Spirit. Izanagi and Izanami rejoiced greatly when they beheld her face, and exclaimed, "Our daughter shall dwell in the Blue Plain of High Heaven, and from there she shall direct the universe." So, they led her to the summit of the mountain, and over the wondrous bridge. The Heavenly Spirits were joyful when they saw Ama-terasu. They said: "You shall mount into the soft blue of the sky, your brilliancy shall light, and your sweet smile shall gladden the Eternal Land and all the world. Fleecy clouds shall be your handmaidens, and sparkling dewdrops your messengers of peace."

The next child of Izanagi and Izanami was a son. As he also was beautiful, with the dream-like beauty of the evening, they placed him in the heavens, as co-ruler with his sister Ama-terasu. His name was Tsuku-yomi, the Moon-God. The god Susa-no-o is another son. Unlike his brother and his sister, he was fond of the shadow and the gloom. When he wept, the grass on the mountainside withered, the flowers were blighted, and men died. Izanagi had little joy in this son, nevertheless he made him ruler of the ocean.

Now that the world was created, the happy life of the God of the Air and the Goddess of the Clouds was over. The consumer, the God of Fire, was born, and Izanami died. She vanished into the deep solitudes of the Kingdom of the Trees, in the country of Kii, and disappeared thence into the lower regions.

Izanagi was sorely troubled because Izanami had been taken from him, and he descended in pursuit of her to the shadowy kingdom where sunshine is unknown. Izanami would have loved to leave that place to rejoin Izanagi on the beautiful earth. Her spirit came to meet him, and in urgent and tender words begged him not to seek her in those dark regions. But the bold god would not be warned. He pressed forward, and, by the light struck from his comb, he sought for his loved one long and earnestly. Grim forms rose to confront him, but he passed them by with kingly disdain. Sounds as of the wailing of lost souls struck his ear, but still he persisted. After endless search, he found his Izanami lying in an attitude of untold despair, but so changed was she, that he gazed intently into her eyes before he could recognize her. Izanami was angry that Izanagi had not listened to her commands, for she knew how **fruitless** his efforts would be. Without the approval of the ruler of the under-world, she could not return to earth, and this consent she had tried in vain to obtain.

....

fruitless useless

Izanagi, hard pressed by the eight monsters who guard the Land of Gloom, had to flee for his life. He defended himself valiantly with his sword. Then he threw down his head-dress, and it was transformed into bunches of purple grapes. He also cast behind him the comb, by means of which he had obtained light, and from it sprang tender shoots of bamboo. While the monsters eagerly devoured the luscious grapes and tender shoots, Izanagi gained the broad flight of steps which led back to earth. At the top he paused and cried to Izanami: "All hope of our reunion is now at an end. Our separation must be eternal."

Stretching far beyond Izanagi lay the ocean, and on its surface was reflected the face of his well-beloved daughter, Ama-terasu. She seemed to speak and beg him to purify himself in the great waters of the sea. As he bathed, his wounds were healed, and a sense of infinite peace stole over him.

The life-work of the Earth-Maker was done. He bestowed the world upon his children, and afterwards crossed, for the last time, the many-colored Bridge of Heaven. The God of the Air now spends his days with the Heaven-Illuminating Spirit in her sun-glorious palace. ❖

The Story of the Beginning

adapted from Asgard Stories: Tales from Norse Mythology
by Mary H. Foster and Mabel H. Cummings

This is the story they told of the Beginning. At first, before living creatures were in the world, it was all rough and without order. Far to the north it was very cold, for ice and snow were everywhere. Toward the south there was fire, and from the meeting of the fire and the cold a thick vapor was formed, from which sprang a huge giant. On looking about for some food, he saw a cow, who was also searching for something to eat. The ice tasted of salt, and when the cow began to lick it, a head appeared. At last the whole figure of a god stood before her.

From these two, the giant and the god, came the two great races of giants and gods, who were always enemies to each other. The giants were constantly trying to break into Asgard, the home of the gods, in the sky. The gods, on the other hand, watched and planned to keep out the giants, and to drive them back to their own stronghold, Utgard. Our world, where men and women lived, was between Utgard and Asgard. It was called Midgard. Around this Midgard world, under the ocean, was coiled a monstrous serpent. It grew so long that his tail grew down his throat. He was called the Midgard serpent.

A wonderful tree, named "**Yggdrasil**," connected all the worlds. This great ash tree had its roots in Utgard. The tops of its branches reached up so high as to overshadow Asgard. Its three main roots were watered by three fountains.

The gods and goddesses, all together, were called the Æsir. The chief and father of them all was Odin. His lofty throne rose high in the midst of Asgard, the sacred city, which the gods had built for their beautiful home.

....

Yggdrasil id-dra-sil

From Asgard, arching over and down to the lower world, was a rainbow bridge, called Bifröst—the trembling bridge.

After the gods had made men and women, and had taught them to dwell on the earth, in the world of Midgard, Odin looked forth one morning from his heavenly seat, to see what further work was waiting for his helping hand.

He noticed, far away below him, a race of small beings. Some of them were busy, doing mischievous deeds, while others sat idle, doing nothing. Odin sent for all these little people to come to him. When they had reached Asgard, and were admitted to his palace of Gladsheim, they entered the great judgment hall where they found all the Æsir sitting, with Father Odin at their head.

The little people waited in a crowd near the door, wondering what was going to happen to them, while Hermod, the messenger of the gods, ran to his master say that they had come.

Then the Allfather spoke to the little dwarfs about their evil deeds among men. He told the naughtiest ones that they must go and live down underground and look after the great furnace fire in the middle of the earth to keep it always burning. Some must get coal to feed the fire, and others still were to have charge of the gold, and silver, and precious stones under the rocks. Not one of these busy dwarfs must ever appear during the day; only by night might they venture to leave their tasks.

"And now," said Odin, turning to the idle ones, "what have you been doing?"

"We were doing nothing at all, so we could not have harmed any one. We pray you to spare us!" cried they.

"Do you not know that those who sit idle when they should be doing good deserve punishment, too?" said Odin. "I shall put you in charge of all the trees and flowers. I shall send one of the Æsir to teach you, so that you may be doing some good in the world."

Then the little elves went to work among the flowers, and Frey, the bright god of summer and sunshine, was a kind master to them. He taught them how to open the folded buds in the sunshine, to fill the honey cups, and lead the bees along the flower passages to find their food, to hatch the birds' eggs, and teach the little ones their songs, and then each night to fetch the water for dewdrops, to be hung on every leaf and blade of grass.

When their work was finished, and the moon had risen, these busy elves and fairies enjoyed many a happy evening, dancing and frisking on the green by moonlight. And so our world of Midgard was filled with busy work and play. ❖

The Twilight of the Gods

adapted from Asgard Stories: Tales from Norse Mythology
by Mary H. Foster and Mabel H. Cummings

Loki and Fenrir, the wolf, were safely bound, each to his separate cliff, but still happiness and peace did not return to Asgard, for Baldur was no longer there, and light and joy had gone from the home of the gods. The Æsir felt that the Twilight of the gods, which Odin knew was to come, must be near.

Soon began a long cold winter. Surely it must be the beginning of the Fimbulwinter, which was to come before the last great battle. From the north came cold blasts of freezing wind. Snow and ice covered the earth. Men could not see the face of the sun or the moon. Everywhere there was darkness. The people grew fierce and unhappy and wicked, for they seemed no longer to love each other. So, the evil deeds of men kept on, and the fierce frost giants grew stronger and stronger. They killed the trees and flowers, and bound the lakes and rivers with icy bands.

Even when summer time came, the cold still held on, and no one could see the green grass or the beautiful golden sunlight. The frost giants were pleased to see the trouble they had brought upon men and hoped they soon could destroy Asgard and the gods.

Three long winters passed, with no light to warm
and brighten the world; after that still three other dreary
winters. Then the eagle who sat on the top of the great
world tree, Yggdrasil, gave a loud, shrill cry. At that the
earth shook, the rocks crumbled and fell, so that Loki and
the wolf were freed from their chains.

The waters of the deep ocean rose and rolled high over
the land. Up above the waves **writhing** out of the deep,
came the monster Midgard serpent to join in the last

....

writhing squirming

battle. Now the enemies of the gods were gathering from all sides—the frost giants, the mountain giants, with Loki, Fenrir, and the Midgard serpent.

Heimdall, the faithful watchman, looked from his watch-tower by the rainbow bridge, and when he saw the host of monsters appearing and raging toward Asgard, he blew his magic horn Giallar which was the signal of warning to the gods.

When Father Odin heard the blast of Heimdall's horn, he rushed to arm himself for the battle. A second call sounded from the Giallar horn, and the gods, with Odin at their head, rode forth from Asgard to meet their foes.

Thor took his place beside Odin, but they were soon parted in the struggle. The thunder-god fell upon his old enemy, the serpent, whom twice before he had tried to slay, and after a fierce fight, he at last conquered and slew the monster; but the poisonous breath from the serpent's mouth overcame the mighty Thor, and he also fell.

Heimdall and Loki came face to face, and each slew the other. Thus, every one of the gods battled each with his foe, till at last the darkness grew deeper, and all, both gods and giants lay dead. Then fire burst forth, raging from Utgard to Asgard—and all the worlds were destroyed in that dreadful day of Ragnarök.

But this was not the end of all: After many months, and years, and even centuries had passed, a new world began to appear, with the fair ocean, and the beautiful land, with a bright, shining sun by day, and the moon and stars by night. Then once more the light and heat from the sun made the grass and trees grow, and the flowers bloom.

Baldur and Hodur came to this beautiful new world and walked and talked together. Thor's sons were there, too, and with them, the hammer, Miölnir, no longer for use against giants, but for helping men build homes.

Two people, a man and a woman, who were kept safe through the raging fire, now came to dwell on the earth, and all their children and grandchildren lived at peace with each other in this beautiful new world.

Baldur and Hodur talked often of the old days when the Æsir dwelt in Asgard, before Loki, the wicked one, brought darkness and trouble to them. With loving words they spoke of Odin and Frigga; and the brave Tyr, who gave his right hand to save the Æsir; of mighty Thor; and faithful Heimdall; of lovely Freyja, with her beautiful necklace; and of fair Iduna's garden, where they used to sit and eat her magic apples. "But still," they said, "we know now that this new world is fairer than the old, and here, also, the loving Allfather watches over his children." ❖

On the Outside Looking In

Law of the Jungle

from The Jungle Book
by Rudyard Kipling

Now this is the Law of the Jungle—as old and as true as the sky;
And the Wolf that shall keep it may prosper, but the Wolf
*   that shall break it must die.*
As the creeper that girdles the tree-trunk, the Law runneth
*   forward and back—*
For the strength of the Pack is the Wolf, and the strength
*   of the Wolf is the Pack.* ❖

Mowgli's Brothers

from The Jungle Book
by Rudyard Kipling

*Now Chil the **Kite** brings home the night*
 That Mang the Bat sets free—
*The herds are shut in **byre** and hut*
 For loosed till dawn are we.
This is the hour of pride and power,
 *Talon and **tush** and claw.*
Oh, hear the call!—Good hunting all
 That keep the Jungle Law!
      —Night Song in the Jungle

kite a bird of prey
byre a cow barn
tush a long, pointed tooth

It was seven o'clock of a very warm evening in the Seeonee hills when Father Wolf woke up from his day's rest, scratched himself, yawned, and spread out his paws one after the other to get rid of the sleepy feeling in their tips. Mother Wolf lay with her big gray nose dropped across her four tumbling, squealing cubs, and the moon shone into the mouth of the cave where they all lived. *"Augrh!"* said Father Wolf, "it is time to hunt again." And he was going to spring downhill when a little shadow with a bushy tail crossed the threshold and whined: "Good luck go with you, O Chief of the Wolves; and good luck and strong white teeth go with noble children, that they may never forget the hungry in this world."

It was the jackal—Tabaqui the Dish-licker—and the wolves of India despise Tabaqui because he runs about making mischief, and telling tales, and eating rags and pieces of leather from the village rubbish heaps. But they are afraid of him too, because Tabaqui, more than anyone else in the jungle, is apt to go mad, and then he forgets that he was ever afraid of anyone, and runs through the forest biting everything in his way. Even the tiger runs and hides when little Tabaqui goes mad, for madness is the most disgraceful thing that can overtake a wild creature. We call it **hydrophobia**, but they call it *dewanee*—the madness—and run.

"Enter, then, and look," said Father Wolf, **stiffly**, "but there is no food here."

"For a wolf, no," said Tabaqui, "but for so mean a person as myself a dry bone is a good feast. Who are we, the *Gidurlog* [the Jackal-People], to pick and choose?" He scuttled to the back of the cave, where he found the bone of a **buck** with some meat on it, and sat cracking the end merrily.

"All thanks for this good meal," he said, licking his lips. "How beautiful are the noble children! How large are their eyes! And so young too! Indeed, indeed, I might have remembered that the children of kings are men from the beginning."

Now, Tabaqui knew as well as anyone else that there is nothing so unlucky as to compliment children to their faces; and it pleased him to see Mother and Father Wolf look uncomfortable.

---

hydrophobia rabies
stiffly proudly; formally
buck a male deer

Tabaqui sat still, rejoicing in the mischief that he had made, and then he said **spitefully**:

"Shere Khan, the Big One, has shifted his hunting grounds. He will hunt among these hills for the next moon, so he has told me."

Shere Khan was the tiger who lived near the Wainganga River, twenty miles away.

"He has no right!" Father Wolf began angrily. "By the Law of the Jungle he has no right to change his **quarters** without due warning. He will frighten every head of game within ten miles, and I—I have to kill for two, these days."

"His mother did not call him Lungri [the Lame One] for nothing," said Mother Wolf, quietly. "He has been lame in one foot from his birth. That is why he has only killed cattle. Now the villagers of the Wainganga are angry with him, and he has come here to make *our* villagers angry. They will **scour** the jungle for him when he is far away, and we and our children must run when the grass is set alight. Indeed, we are very grateful to Shere Khan!"

"Shall I tell him of your gratitude?" said Tabaqui.

"Out!" snapped Father Wolf. "Out and hunt with thy master. Thou hast done harm enough for one night."

"I go," said Tabaqui, quietly. "Ye can hear Shere Khan below in the thickets. I might have saved myself the message."

spitefully in an intentionally mean and hurtful way
quarters the place where one lives
scour to search carefully

Father Wolf listened, and below in the valley that ran down to a little river, he heard the dry, angry, snarly, singsong whine of a tiger who has caught nothing and does not care if all the jungle knows it.

"The fool!" said Father Wolf. "To begin a night's work with that noise! Does he think that our buck are like his fat Waingunga **bullocks**?"

"*Hsh*. It is neither bullock nor buck he hunts tonight," said Mother Wolf. "It is Man."

The whine had changed to a sort of humming purr that seemed to come from every quarter of the compass. It was the noise that bewilders woodcutters and gypsies sleeping in the open, and makes them run sometimes into the very mouth of the tiger.

"Man!" said Father Wolf, showing all his white teeth. "*Faugh*! Are there not enough beetles and frogs in the tanks that he must eat Man, and on our ground too!"

The Law of the Jungle, which never orders anything without a reason, forbids every beast to eat Man except when he is killing to show his children how to kill, and then he must hunt outside the hunting grounds of his pack or tribe. The real reason for this is that man-killing means, sooner or later, the arrival of white men on elephants, with guns, and hundreds of brown men with gongs and rockets and torches. Then everybody in the jungle suffers. The

....

bullocks young bulls

reason the beasts give among themselves is that Man is the weakest and most defenseless of all living things, and it is unsportsmanlike to touch him. They say too—and it is true—that man-eaters become mangy, and lose their teeth.

The purr grew louder, and ended in the full-throated "*Aaarh*!" of the tiger's charge.

Then there was a howl—an untigerish howl—from Shere Khan. "He has missed," said Mother Wolf. "What is it?"

Father Wolf ran out a few paces and heard Shere Khan muttering and mumbling savagely, as he tumbled about in the scrub.

"The fool has had no more sense than to jump at a woodcutters' campfire, and has burned his feet," said Father Wolf with a grunt. "Tabaqui is with him."

"Something is coming uphill," said Mother Wolf, twitching one ear. "Get ready."

The bushes rustled a little in the thicket, and Father Wolf dropped with his haunches under him, ready for his leap. Then, if you had been watching, you would have seen the most wonderful thing in the world—the wolf checked in midspring. He made his bound before he saw what it was he was jumping at, and then he tried to stop himself. The result was that he shot up straight into the air for four or five feet, landing almost where he left ground.

"Man!" he snapped. "A man's cub. Look!"

Directly in front of him, holding on by a low branch, stood a naked brown baby who could just walk—as soft and as dimpled a little atom as ever came to a wolf's cave at night. He looked up into Father Wolf's face, and laughed.

"Is that a man's cub?" said Mother Wolf. "I have never seen one. Bring it here."

A wolf accustomed to moving his own cubs can, if necessary, mouth an egg without breaking it, and though Father Wolf's jaws closed right on the child's back, not a tooth even scratched the skin, as he laid it down among the cubs.

"How little! How naked, and—how bold!" said Mother Wolf softly. The baby was pushing his way between the cubs to get close to the warm hide. "*Ahai!* He is taking his meal with the others. And so this is a man's cub. Now, was there ever a wolf that could boast of a man's cub among her children?"

"I have heard now and again of such a thing, but never in our pack or in my time," said Father Wolf. "He is altogether without hair, and I could kill him with a touch of my foot. But see, he looks up and is not afraid."

The moonlight was blocked out of the mouth of the cave, for Shere Khan's great square head and shoulders were thrust into the entrance. Tabaqui, behind him, was squeaking: "My lord, my lord, it went in here!"

"Shere Khan does us great honor," said Father Wolf, but his eyes were very angry. "What does Shere Khan need?"

"My **quarry**. A man's cub went this way," said Shere Khan. "Its parents have run off. Give it to me."

Shere Khan had jumped at a woodcutters' campfire, as Father Wolf had said, and was furious from the pain of his burned feet. But Father Wolf knew that the mouth of the cave was too narrow for a tiger to come in by. Even where he was, Shere Khan's shoulders and forepaws were cramped for want of room, as a man's would be if he tried to fight in a barrel.

"The wolves are a free people," said Father Wolf. "They take orders from the head of the pack, and not from any striped cattle-killer. The man's cub is ours—to kill if we choose."

"Ye choose and ye do not choose! What talk is this of choosing? By the bull that I killed, am I to stand nosing into your dog's den for my fair dues? It is I, Shere Khan, who speak!"

The tiger's roar filled the cave with thunder. Mother Wolf shook herself clear of the cubs and sprang forward, her eyes, like two green moons in the darkness, facing the blazing eyes of Shere Khan.

"And it is I, Raksha [the Demon], who answer. The man's cub is mine, Lungri—mine to me! He shall not be killed. He shall live to run with the pack and to hunt with the pack; and in the end, look you, hunter of little naked

---

quarry prey; an animal hunted or chased

cubs—frog-eater—fish-killer—he shall hunt *thee*! Now
get hence, or by the **sambur** that I killed (*I* eat no starved
cattle), back thou goest to thy mother, burned beast of the
jungle, lamer than ever thou camest into the world! Go!"

Father Wolf looked on amazed. He had almost forgotten
the days when he won Mother Wolf in fair fight from five
other wolves, when she ran in the pack and was not called
the Demon for compliment's sake. Shere Khan might have
faced Father Wolf, but he could not stand up against
Mother Wolf, for he knew that where he was she had all the
advantage of the ground, and would fight to the death. So
he backed out of the cave mouth growling, and when he
was clear he shouted:

"Each dog barks in his own yard! We will see what the
pack will say to this **fostering** of man-cubs. The cub is
mine, and to my teeth he will come in the end, O bush-
tailed thieves!"

Mother Wolf threw herself down panting among the
cubs, and Father Wolf said to her gravely:

"Shere Khan speaks this much truth. The cub must be
shown to the pack. Wilt thou still keep him, Mother?"

"Keep him!" she gasped. "He came naked, by night,
alone and very hungry; yet he was not afraid! Look, he has
pushed one of my babes to one side already. And that lame

....

get hence go away
sambur a large Asian deer (also spelled *sambar*)
fostering the act of taking care of

butcher would have killed him and would have run off to the Wainganga while the villagers here hunted through all our lairs in revenge! Keep him? Assuredly I will keep him. Lie still, little frog. O thou Mowgli—for Mowgli the Frog I will call thee—the time will come when thou wilt hunt Shere Khan as he has hunted thee."

"But what will our pack say?" said Father Wolf.

The Law of the Jungle lays down very clearly that any wolf may, when he marries, withdraw from the pack he belongs to; but as soon as his cubs are old enough to stand on their feet he must bring them to the pack council, which is generally held once a month at full moon, in order that the other wolves may identify them. After that inspection the cubs are free to run where they please, and until they have killed their first buck no excuse is accepted if a grown wolf of the pack kills one of them. The punishment is death where the murderer can be found; and if you think for a minute you will see that this must be so.

Father Wolf waited till his cubs could run a little, and then on the night of the pack meeting took them and Mowgli and Mother Wolf to the Council Rock—a hilltop covered with stones and boulders where a hundred wolves could hide. Akela, the great gray Lone Wolf, who led all the pack by strength and cunning, lay out at full length on his rock, and below him sat forty or more wolves of every size and color, from badger-colored veterans who could handle a buck alone to young black three-year-olds who thought they could. The Lone Wolf had led them for a year now. He had fallen twice into a wolf trap in his youth, and once he had been beaten and left for dead; so he knew the manners and customs of men. There was very little talking at the rock. The cubs tumbled over each other in the center of the circle where their mothers and fathers sat, and now and again a senior wolf would go quietly up to a cub, look at him carefully, and return to his place on noiseless feet. Sometimes a mother would push her cub far out into the moonlight, to be sure that he had not been overlooked. Akela from his rock would cry: "Ye know the Law—ye know the Law. Look well, O wolves!" And the anxious mothers would take up the call: "Look—look well, O wolves!"

At last—and Mother Wolf's neck bristles lifted as the time came—Father Wolf pushed "Mowgli the Frog," as they called him, into the center, where he sat laughing and playing with some pebbles that glistened in the moonlight.

Akela never raised his head from his paws, but went on with the monotonous cry: "Look well!" A muffled roar came up from behind the rocks—the voice of Shere Khan crying: "The cub is mine. Give him to me. What have the Free People to do with a man's cub?"

Akela never even twitched his ears. All he said was: "Look well, O wolves! What have the Free People to do with the orders of any save the Free People? Look well!"

There was a chorus of deep growls, and a young wolf in his fourth year flung back Shere Khan's question to Akela:

"What have the Free People to do with a man's cub?" Now the Law of the Jungle lays down that if there is any dispute as to the right of a cub to be accepted by the pack, he must be spoken for by at least two members of the pack who are not his father and mother.

"Who speaks for this cub?" said Akela. "Among the Free People who speaks?" There was no answer, and Mother Wolf got ready for what she knew would be her last fight, if things came to fighting.

Then the only other creature who is allowed at the pack council—Baloo, the sleepy brown bear who teaches the wolf cubs the Law of the Jungle: old Baloo, who can come and go where he pleases because he eats only nuts and roots and honey—rose upon his hind quarters and grunted.

"The man's cub—the man's cub?" he said. "*I* speak for the man's cub. There is no harm in a man's cub. I have no gift of words, but I speak the truth. Let him run with the pack, and be entered with the others. I myself will teach him."

"We need yet another," said Akela. "Baloo has spoken, and he is our teacher for the young cubs. Who speaks besides Baloo?"

A black shadow dropped down into the circle. It was Bagheera the Black Panther, inky black all over, but with the panther markings showing up in certain lights like the pattern of watered silk. Everybody knew Bagheera, and nobody cared to cross his path, for he was as cunning as

Tabaqui, as bold as the wild buffalo, and as reckless as the wounded elephant. But he had a voice as soft as wild honey dripping from a tree, and a skin softer than down.

"O Akela, and ye the Free People," he purred, "I have no right in your assembly, but the Law of the Jungle says that if there is a doubt which is not a killing matter in regard to a new cub, the life of that cub may be bought at a price. And the Law does not say who may or may not pay that price. Am I right?"

"Good! Good!" said the young wolves, who are always hungry. "Listen to Bagheera. The cub can be bought for a price. It is the Law."

"Knowing that I have no right to speak here, I ask your leave."

"Speak then," cried twenty voices.

"To kill a naked cub is shame. Besides, he may make better sport for you when he is grown. Baloo has spoken in his behalf. Now to Baloo's word I will add one bull, and a fat one, newly killed, not half a mile from here, if ye will accept the man's cub according to the Law. Is it difficult?"

There was a clamor of **scores** of voices, saying: "What matter? He will die in the winter rains. He will scorch in the sun. What harm can a naked frog do us? Let him run with the pack. Where is the bull, Bagheera? Let him be accepted." And then came Akela's deep bay, crying: "Look well—look well, O wolves!"

....

scores many (one score = twenty)

Mowgli was still deeply interested in the pebbles, and he did not notice when the wolves came and looked at him one by one. At last they all went down the hill for the dead bull, and only Akela, Bagheera, Baloo, and Mowgli's own wolves were left. Shere Khan roared still in the night, for he was very angry that Mowgli had not been handed over to him.

"Ay, roar well," said Bagheera, under his whiskers, "for the time comes when this naked thing will make thee roar to another tune, or I know nothing of man."

"It was well done," said Akela. "Men and their cubs are very wise. He may be a help in time."

"Truly, a help in time of need, for none can hope to lead the pack forever," said Bagheera.

Akela said nothing. He was thinking of the time that comes to every leader of every pack when his strength goes from him and he gets feebler and feebler, till at last he is killed by the wolves and a new leader comes up—to be killed in his turn.

"Take him away," he said to Father Wolf, "and train him as befits one of the Free People."

And that is how Mowgli was entered into the Seeonee Wolf Pack for the price of a bull and on Baloo's good word.

Now you must be content to skip ten or eleven whole years, and only guess at all the wonderful life that Mowgli led among the wolves, because if it were written out it would fill ever so many books. He grew up with the cubs, though they, of course, were grown wolves almost before he was a child, and Father Wolf taught him his business, and the meaning of things in the jungle, till every rustle in the grass, every breath of the warm night air, every note of the owls above his head, every scratch of a bat's claws as it roosted for a while in a tree, and every splash of every little fish jumping in a pool, meant just as much to him as the work of his office means to a business man. When he was not learning he sat out in the sun and slept, and ate and went to sleep again; when he felt dirty or hot he swam in the forest pools; and when he wanted honey (Baloo told him that honey and nuts were just as pleasant to eat as raw meat) he climbed up for it, and that Bagheera showed him how to do. Bagheera would lie out on a branch and call: "Come along, Little Brother," and at first Mowgli would cling like the **sloth**, but afterward he would fling himself through the branches almost as boldly as the gray ape. He took his place at the Council Rock, too, when the pack met, and there he discovered that if he stared hard at any wolf, the wolf would be forced to drop his eyes, and so he used to stare for fun. At other times he would pick the long thorns out of the pads of his friends, for wolves suffer terribly from thorns and burs in their coats. He would go down the hillside into the **cultivated** lands by night, and look very curiously at the villagers in their huts, but he

sloth an animal of the tropical forests that hangs from trees by its claws
cultivated farmed

had a mistrust of men because Bagheera showed him a square box with a drop-gate so cunningly hidden in the jungle that he nearly walked into it, and told him that it was a trap. He loved better than anything else to go with Bagheera into the dark warm heart of the forest, to sleep all through the drowsy day, and at night see how Bagheera did his killing. Bagheera killed right and left as he felt hungry, and so did Mowgli—with one exception. As soon as he was old enough to understand things, Bagheera told him that he must never touch cattle because he had been bought into the pack at the price of a bull's life. "All the jungle is thine," said Bagheera, "and thou canst kill everything that *thou* art strong enough to kill; but for the sake of the bull that bought thee thou must never kill or eat any cattle young or old. That is the Law of the Jungle." Mowgli obeyed faithfully.

And he grew and grew strong as a boy must grow who does not know that he is learning any lessons, and who has nothing in the world to think of except things to eat.

Mother Wolf told him once or twice that Shere Khan was not a creature to be trusted, and that someday he must kill Shere Khan. But though a young wolf would have remembered that advice every hour, Mowgli forgot it because he was only a boy—though he would have called himself a wolf if he had been able to speak in any human tongue.

Shere Khan was always crossing his path in the jungle, for as Akela grew older and feebler the lame tiger had come to be great friends with the younger wolves of the pack, who followed him for scraps, a thing Akela would never have allowed if he had dared to push his authority to the proper bounds. Then Shere Khan would flatter them and wonder that such fine young hunters were content to be led by a dying wolf and a man's cub. "They tell me," Shere Khan would say, "that at council ye dare not look him between the eyes." And the young wolves would growl and bristle.

Bagheera, who had eyes and ears everywhere, knew something of this, and once or twice he told Mowgli in so many words that Shere Khan would kill him someday. And Mowgli would laugh and answer: "I have the pack and I have thee; and Baloo, though he is so lazy, might strike a blow or two for my sake. Why should I be afraid?"

It was one very warm day that a new **notion** came to Bagheera—born of something that he had heard. Perhaps Sahi the Porcupine had told him; but he said to Mowgli when they were deep in the jungle, as the boy lay with his head on Bagheera's beautiful black skin: "Little Brother, how often have I told thee that Shere Khan is thy enemy?"

"As many times as there are nuts on that palm," said Mowgli, who, naturally, could not count. "What of it? I am

....

notion an idea

sleepy, Bagheera, and Shere Khan is all long tail and loud talk—like Mor, the Peacock."

"But this is no time for sleeping. Baloo knows it; I know it; the pack knows it; and even the foolish, foolish deer know. Tabaqui has told thee, too."

"Ho! Ho!" said Mowgli. "Tabaqui came to me not long ago with some rude talk that I was a naked man's cub and not fit to dig pignuts; but I caught Tabaqui by the tail and swung him twice against a palm tree to teach him better manners."

"That was foolishness, for though Tabaqui is a mischief maker, he would have told thee of something that concerned thee closely. Open those eyes, Little Brother. Shere Khan dare not kill thee in the jungle; but remember, Akela is very old, and soon the day comes when he cannot kill his buck, and then he will be leader no more. Many of the wolves that looked thee over when thou wast brought to the council first are old too, and the young wolves believe, as Shere Khan has taught them, that a man-cub has no place with the pack. In a little time thou wilt be a man."

"And what is a man that he should not run with his brothers?" said Mowgli. "I was born in the jungle. I have obeyed the Law of the Jungle, and there is no wolf of ours from whose paws I have not pulled a thorn. Surely they are my brothers!"

Bagheera stretched himself at full length and half shut his eyes. "Little Brother," said he, "feel under my jaw."

Mowgli put up his strong brown hand, and just under Bagheera's silky chin, where the giant rolling muscles were all hid by the glossy hair, he came upon a little bald spot.

"There is no one in the jungle that knows that I, Bagheera, carry that mark—the mark of the collar. And yet, Little Brother, I was born among men, and it was among men that my mother died—in the cages of the king's palace at Oodeypore. It was because of this that I paid the price for thee at the council when thou wast a little naked cub. Yes, I too was born among men. I had never seen the jungle. They fed me behind bars from an iron pan till one night I felt that I was Bagheera—the Panther—and no man's plaything, and I broke the silly lock with one blow of my paw and came away. And because I had learned the ways of men, I became more terrible in the jungle than Shere Khan. Is it not so?"

"Yes," said Mowgli, "all the jungle fears Bagheera—all except Mowgli."

"Oh, *thou* art a man's cub," said the black panther, very tenderly, "and even as I returned to my jungle, so thou must go back to men at last—to the men who are thy brothers—if thou art not killed in the council."

"But why—but why should any wish to kill me?" said Mowgli.

"Look at me," said Bagheera, and Mowgli looked at him steadily between the eyes. The big panther turned his head away in half a minute.

"*That* is why," he said, shifting his paw on the leaves. "Not even I can look thee between the eyes, and I was born among men, and I love thee, Little Brother. The others they hate thee because their eyes cannot meet thine; because thou art wise; because thou hast pulled out thorns from their feet—because thou art a man."

"I did not know these things," said Mowgli, sullenly, and he frowned under his heavy black eyebrows.

"What is the Law of the Jungle? Strike first and then give tongue. By thy very carelessness they know that thou art a man. But be wise. It is in my heart that when Akela misses his next kill—and at each hunt it costs him more to pin the buck—the pack will turn against him and against thee. They will hold a jungle council at the rock, and then—and then—I have it!" said Bagheera, leaping up. "Go thou down quickly to the men's huts in the valley, and take some of the Red Flower which they grow there, so that when the time comes thou mayest have even a stronger friend than I or Baloo or those of the pack that love thee. Get the Red Flower."

By Red Flower Bagheera meant fire, only no creature in the jungle will call fire by its proper name. Every beast lives in deadly fear of it, and invents a hundred ways of describing it.

"The Red Flower?" said Mowgli. "That grows outside their huts in the twilight. I will get some."

"There speaks the man's cub," said Bagheera, proudly. "Remember that it grows in little pots. Get one swiftly, and keep it by thee for time of need."

"Good!" said Mowgli. "I go. But art thou sure, O my Bagheera"—he slipped his arm round the splendid neck and looked deep into the big eyes—"art thou sure that all this is Shere Khan's doing?"

"By the broken lock that freed me, I am sure, Little Brother."

"Then, by the bull that bought me, I will pay Shere Khan full **tale** for this, and it may be a little over," said Mowgli, and he bounded away.

"That is a man. That is all a man," said Bagheera to himself, lying down again. "Oh, Shere Khan, never was a blacker hunting than that frog hunt of thine ten years ago!"

Mowgli was far and far through the forest, running hard, and his heart was hot in him. He came to the cave as the evening mist rose, and drew breath, and looked down the valley. The cubs were out, but Mother Wolf, at the back of the cave, knew by his breathing that something was troubling her frog.

"What is it, son?" she said.

"Some bat's chatter of Shere Khan," he called back. "I hunt among the plowed fields tonight." And he plunged

....

tale total; amount

downward through the bushes, to the stream at the bottom of the valley. There he checked, for he heard the yell of the pack hunting, heard the bellow of a hunted sambur, and the snort as the buck turned at bay. Then there were wicked, bitter howls from the young wolves: "Akela! Akela! Let the Lone Wolf show his strength. Room for the leader of the pack! Spring, Akela!"

The Lone Wolf must have sprung and missed his hold, for Mowgli heard the snap of his teeth and then a yelp as the sambur knocked him over with his forefoot.

He did not wait for anything more, but dashed on; and the yells grew fainter behind him as he ran into the croplands where the villagers lived.

"Bagheera spoke truth," he panted, as he nestled down in some cattle **fodder** by the window of a hut. "Tomorrow is one day both for Akela and for me."

Then he pressed his face close to the window and watched the fire on the hearth. He saw the **husbandman's** wife get up and feed it in the night with black lumps; and when the morning came and the mists were all white and cold, he saw the man's child pick up a wicker pot plastered inside with earth, fill it with lumps of red-hot charcoal, put it under his blanket, and go out to tend the cows in the byre.

....

fodder food for cattle, horses, sheep; hay
husbandman farmer

"Is that all?" said Mowgli. "If a cub can do it, there is nothing to fear." So he strode round the corner and met the boy, took the pot from his hand, and disappeared into the mist while the boy howled with fear.

"They are very like me," said Mowgli, blowing into the pot as he had seen the woman do. "This thing will die if I do not give it things to eat." And he dropped twigs and dried bark on the red stuff. Halfway up the hill he met Bagheera with the morning dew shining like moonstones on his coat.

"Akela has missed," said the panther. "They would have killed him last night, but they needed thee also. They were looking for thee on the hill."

"I was among the plowed lands. I am ready. See!" Mowgli held up the fire-pot.

"Good! Now, I have seen men thrust a dry branch into that stuff, and **presently** the Red Flower blossomed at the end of it. Art thou not afraid?"

"No. Why should I fear? I remember now—if it is not a dream—how, before I was a wolf, I lay beside the Red Flower, and it was warm and pleasant."

All that day Mowgli sat in the cave tending his fire-pot and dipping dry branches into it to see how they looked. He found a branch that satisfied him, and in the evening when Tabaqui came to the cave and told him

presently soon

rudely enough that he was wanted at the Council Rock, he laughed till Tabaqui ran away. Then Mowgli went to the council, still laughing.

Akela the Lone Wolf lay by the side of his rock as a sign that the leadership of the pack was open, and Shere Khan with his following of scrap-fed wolves walked to and fro openly being flattered. Bagheera lay close to Mowgli, and the fire-pot was between Mowgli's knees. When they were all gathered together, Shere Khan began to speak—a thing he would never have dared to do when Akela was in his prime.

"He has no right," whispered Bagheera. "Say so. He is a dog's son. He will be frightened."

Mowgli sprang to his feet. "Free People," he cried, "does Shere Khan lead the pack? What has a tiger to do with our leadership?"

"Seeing that the leadership is yet open, and being asked to speak—" Shere Khan began.

"By whom?" said Mowgli. "Are we all jackals, to fawn on this cattle-butcher? The leadership of the pack is with the pack alone."

There were yells of "Silence, thou man's cub!" "Let him speak. He has kept our Law." And at last the seniors of the Pack thundered: "Let the Dead Wolf speak." When a leader of the pack has missed his kill, he is called the Dead Wolf as long as he lives, which is not long.

Akela raised his old head wearily:

"Free People, and ye too, jackals of Shere Khan, for twelve seasons I have led ye to and from the kill, and in all that time not one has been trapped or maimed. Now I have missed my kill. Ye know how that plot was made. Ye know how ye brought me up to an untried buck to make my weakness known. It was cleverly done. Your right is to kill me here on the Council Rock, now. Therefore, I ask, who comes to make an end of the Lone Wolf? For it is my right, by the Law of the Jungle, that ye come one by one."

There was a long hush, for no single wolf cared to fight Akela to the death. Then Shere Khan roared: "Bah! What have we to do with this toothless fool? He is doomed to die! It is the man-cub who has lived too long. Free People, he was my meat from the first. Give him to me. I am weary of this man-wolf folly. He has troubled the jungle for ten seasons. Give me the man-cub, or I will hunt here always, and not give you one bone. He is a man, a man's child, and from the marrow of my bones I hate him!"

Then more than half the pack yelled: "A man! A man! What has a man to do with us? Let him go to his own place."

"And turn all the people of the villages against us?" clamored Shere Khan. "No! Give him to me. He is a man, and none of us can look him between the eyes."

Akela lifted his head again, and said: "He has eaten our food. He has slept with us. He has driven game for us. He has broken no word of the Law of the Jungle."

"Also, I paid for him with a bull when he was accepted. The worth of a bull is little, but Bagheera's honor is something that he will perhaps fight for," said Bagheera in his gentlest voice.

"A bull paid ten years ago!" the pack snarled. "What do we care for bones ten years old?"

"Or for a **pledge**?" said Bagheera, his white teeth bared under his lip. "Well are ye called the Free People!"

"No man's cub can run with the People of the Jungle," howled Shere Khan. "Give him to me!"

"He is our brother in all but blood," Akela went on, "and ye would kill him here! In truth, I have lived too long. Some of ye are eaters of cattle, and of others I have heard that, under Shere Khan's teaching, ye go by dark night and snatch children from the villager's doorstep. Therefore I know ye to be cowards, and it is to cowards I speak. It is certain that I must die, and my life is of no worth, or I would offer that in the man-cub's place. But for the sake of the honor of the pack—a little matter that by being without a leader ye have forgotten—I promise that if ye let the man-cub go to his own place, I will not, when my time comes to die, bare one tooth against ye. I will die without fighting. That will at least save the pack three lives.

------

pledge a promise

More I cannot do; but if ye will, I can save ye the shame that comes of killing a brother against whom there is no fault—a brother spoken for and bought into the pack according to the Law of the Jungle."

"He is a man—a man—a man!" snarled the Pack. And most of the wolves began to gather round Shere Khan, whose tail was beginning to switch.

"Now the business is in thy hands," said Bagheera to Mowgli. "*We* can do no more except fight."

Mowgli stood upright—the fire-pot in his hands. Then he stretched out his arms, and yawned in the face of the council. But he was furious with rage and sorrow, for, wolflike, the wolves had never told him how they hated him. "Listen you!" he cried. "There is no need for this dog's **jabber**. Ye have told me so often tonight that I am a man (and indeed I would have been a wolf with you to my life's end) that I feel your words are true. So I do not call ye my brothers any more, but sag [dogs], as a man should. What ye will do, and what ye will not do, is not yours to say. That matter is with *me*. And that we may see the matter more plainly, I, the man, have brought here a little of the Red Flower which ye, dogs, fear."

He flung the fire-pot on the ground, and some of the red coals lit a tuft of dried moss that flared up, as all the council drew back in terror before the leaping flames.

....

jabber nonsense; chatter

Mowgli thrust his dead branch into the fire till the twigs lit and crackled, and whirled it above his head among the **cowering** wolves.

"Thou art the master," said Bagheera in an **undertone**. "Save Akela from the death. He was ever thy friend."

Akela, the grim old wolf who had never asked for mercy in his life, gave one piteous look at Mowgli as the boy stood all naked, his long black hair tossing over his shoulders in the light of the blazing branch that made the shadows jump and quiver.

"Good!" said Mowgli, staring round slowly. "I see that ye are dogs. I go from you to my own people—if they be my own people. The jungle is shut to me, and I must forget your talk and your companionship; but I will be more merciful than ye are. Because I was all but your brother in blood, I promise that when I am a man among men I will not betray ye to men as ye have betrayed me." He kicked the fire with his foot, and the sparks flew up. "There shall be no war between any of us in the pack. But here is a debt to pay before I go." He strode forward to where Shere Khan sat blinking stupidly at the flames, and caught him by the tuft on his chin. Bagheera followed in case of accidents. "Up, dog!" Mowgli cried. "Up, when a man speaks, or I will set that coat ablaze!"

....

cowering shrinking back in fear
undertone a low or soft voice

Shere Khan's ears lay flat back on his head, and he shut his eyes, for the blazing branch was very near.

"This cattle-killer said he would kill me in the council because he had not killed me when I was a cub. Thus and thus, then, do we beat dogs when we are men. Stir a whisker, Lungri, and I ram the Red Flower down thy **gullet**!" He beat Shere Khan over the head with the branch, and the tiger whimpered and whined in an agony of fear.

"*Pah*! Singed jungle cat—go now! But remember when next I come to the Council Rock, as a man should come, it will be with Shere Khan's hide on my head. For the rest, Akela goes free to live as he pleases. Ye will not kill him, because that is not my will. Nor do I think that ye will sit here any longer, lolling out your tongues as though ye were somebodies, instead of dogs whom I drive out— thus! Go!" The fire was burning furiously at the end of the branch, and Mowgli struck right and left round the circle, and the wolves ran howling with the sparks burning their fur. At last there were only Akela, Bagheera, and perhaps ten wolves that had taken Mowgli's part. Then something began to hurt Mowgli inside him, as he had never been hurt in his life before, and he caught his breath and sobbed, and the tears ran down his face.

"What is it? What is it?" he said. "I do not wish to leave the jungle, and I do not know what this is. Am I dying, Bagheera?"

gullet throat

"No, Little Brother. That is only tears such as men use," said Bagheera. "Now I know thou art a man, and a man's cub no longer. The jungle is shut indeed to thee **henceforward**. Let them fall, Mowgli. They are only tears." So Mowgli sat and cried as though his heart would break; and he had never cried in all his life before.

"Now," he said, "I will go to men. But first I must say farewell to my mother." And he went to the cave where she lived with Father Wolf, and he cried on her coat, while the four cubs howled miserably.

"Ye will not forget me?" said Mowgli.

"Never while we can follow a trail," said the cubs. "Come to the foot of the hill when thou art a man, and we will talk to thee; and we will come into the croplands to play with thee by night."

"Come soon!" said Father Wolf. "Oh, wise little frog, come again soon, for we be old, thy mother and I."

"Come soon," said Mother Wolf, "little naked son of mine, for, listen, child of man, I loved thee more than ever I loved my cubs."

"I will surely come," said Mowgli, "and when I come it will be to lay out Shere Khan's hide upon the Council Rock. Do not forget me! Tell them in the jungle never to forget me!"

The dawn was beginning to break when Mowgli went down the hillside alone, to meet those mysterious things that are called men. ❖

....

henceforward from this time on

Hunting Song of the Seeonee Pack

from The Jungle Book
by Rudyard Kipling

*As the dawn was breaking the sambur **belled***
Once, twice, and again!
And a doe leaped up and a doe leaped up
From the pond in the wood where the wild deer sup.
This I, scouting alone, beheld
Once, twice, and again!

As the dawn was breaking the sambur belled
Once, twice, and again!
And a wolf stole back and a wolf stole back
To carry the word to the waiting pack,
And we sought and we found and we bayed on his track
Once, twice, and again!

As the dawn was breaking the wolf pack yelled
Once, twice, and again!
Feet in the jungle that leave no mark!
Eyes that can see in the dark—the dark!
*Tongue—**give tongue** to it! Hark! O hark!*
Once, twice, and again! ❖

belled bellowed; cried out
give tongue an expression meaning "speak it, say it aloud"

The Difficult Path

by Grace Lin

When I was sold to the Li family, my mother let Mrs. Li take me only after she'd promised that I would be taught to read. "Her mother had fourteen other children starving and clinging to her, yet she was still insisting that I promise." Mrs. Li sniffed and began a high-pitched imitation. "'Promise me that when she's six, you'll have her taught to read! On your ancestors' grave! Promise!'"

"You didn't have to agree," Aunty Wang replied peevishly. This was a story she had already heard many times.

"A girl! Learn to read! What a waste!" Mrs. Li continued, her annoyance at the past greater than Aunty Wang's with the present. "Just because the mother had been a scholar's daughter!"

"Then you shouldn't have lied," Aunty Wang said, rolling her eyes. She helped herself to some honeyed lychees I held.

"I thought she would never know!" Mrs. Li said. "I just said yes so that I could take the baby and go."

I made a soft coughing noise and placed the tray on the table.

"Mrs. Li," I said as I bowed low, "Teacher is here."

She snorted with irritation and waved her arm, her voluminous silk sleeve flapping like a flag of surrender. "Go," she dismissed me.

I hid my smile and tried to walk humbly, as all the brow-beaten servants were supposed to do. Unlike Aunty Wang, however, I was not tired of Mrs. Li's complaining story. I had no memory of my mother, but hearing how she had dared to make demands of the **formidable** Mrs. Li on my behalf always made me feel a sense of pride. Despite my mother's poor circumstances, she must have been spirited.

And perhaps it was my mother's spirit that forced Mrs. Li to keep her promise. For on the day I turned six, a

---

formidable inspiring fear

new tutor came to the House of Li. As I cringed during my daily duty of emptying the chamber pots, I saw the top of his black scholar's hat glide slowly past the family shrine into the schoolroom. He had come for Mrs. Li's **repulsive** only son, FuDing, of course. The learned scholar was yet another tutor hired in hopes that FuDing could be taught something. The last two teachers had departed in disgrace as well as anger. For, because FuDing remained unable to read a single poem, Mrs. Li had also refused the tutors' pay.

My birthday and a new tutor's entry should have been of small consequence to the House of Li, except it was also on that day that the incense of the ancestral shrine refused to light. Master Li tried again and again, but no matter how large a flame he held, the incense would not burn. In desperation, Master Li turned to the new tutor for answers.

"It is apparent," the scholar said, "that you or someone in your household has shamed your ancestors. Perhaps someone has stolen something or has broken a promise."

"Of course." Master Li nodded with respect. Then he snapped at Mrs. Li. "Wife! We have angered our ancestors! What have you done?"

The House of Li roared into a typhoon as all, from the head cook to the lowliest servant (me), were questioned. When it was discovered that it was my sixth birthday, Mrs. Li remembered her promise to my mother, then paled and swayed like a blanched stalk of bamboo.

---

repulsive causing disgust

"It couldn't be ...," she said in horror.

But it could be and probably was, the new tutor said, and immediately quoted his price for two students. Mrs. Li, still **aghast** at the revelation and fending off insults from her husband, did not even haggle over the price. (She did try later, claiming that as a girl I should be cheaper, but he responded the because I was a girl he should be paid more, as he was making an exception, so the matter was dropped.) And I began my education.

That was over six years ago. It was also over six years ago that I saw my Teacher walk in with a new pair of shoes. Those shoes glided on the smooth stone floor, only hesitating as he paused in front of the shrine. With a sharp glance around, he quickly changed the incense—insuring my lessons and his large salary.

"You are late, Lingsi!" Teacher said, but without anger. He knew Mrs. Li was always the reason for my tardiness.

"Lingsi is late!" FuDing sneered. I tried to consider FuDing with kindness, for it was his inability to read little more than his name that had granted me so many years of lessons. But it was difficult. His body had, over the years, grown into a man's, but he was still the same lazy, spoiled brat he had been as a boy. If anything, the years had made him even more horrible, for now he had a **vicious** streak

---

aghast horrified
vicious cruel

that delighted in cruelty. I couldn't help shivering when I saw that he was pulling the legs off crickets again.

"Today's poem," Teacher said, ignoring FuDing, "is 'The Difficult Path' by Li Po."

I knelt at the table and began to read.

> *"I will ride the winds and*
> ***Surmount*** *endless waves.*
> *Setting sail on the vast ocean,*
> *I will one day reach*
> *The distant shores."*

"The ocean," I murmured. I had been outside the walled estate of the House of Li only a handful of times. However, one time Shuwan, the head cook, and I had been sent to town to buy pepper, and I had caught a glimpse of the sea. But only a glimpse, for when I tried to see more, I was yanked away. Shuwan had a terror of pirates and was convinced that just looking at the sea could make them appear.

"Li Po writes of endless hardships," Teacher said, "but you also feel his **valiant** spirit. I hope this is something you remember, Lingsi."

I looked up at him, the question in my eyes, since I dared not ask with my voice.

....

surmount overcome
valiant brave

"Today is our last lesson," Teacher said. "Mrs. Li has informed me that FuDing will soon be of marrying age and his time must now be spent in . . . other ways."

We both glanced at FuDing, who was creating a pile of dead insects, and then quickly looked away. My eyes filled with tears. I had known that these lessons would not continue forever, but now that they were ending, I felt I could not bear it.

"You have learned much, Lingsi," Teacher said to me kindly. "You are a very smart and clever pupil. If you had been a boy, I have no doubt you would have won honors at the Imperial Examination."

I tried to smile but could only bow my head. I felt Teacher's hand gently rest upon it.

"Mencius, the Second Sage, said that there are three joys in this world," he said. "Health, a clear conscience, and teaching those who are worthy. Teaching you has been a joy, Lingsi."

My tears continued to drop long after our last lesson, long after Teacher had left the House of Li and I had swept up FuDing's collection of insects. They even continued as I scrubbed the pots in the kitchen, much to the annoyance of the other servants.

"Stop your crying," Bisi snapped, carrying over dirty bowls for me to wash. "We've got enough to do without listening to your sniffling."

"Look at me," Shuwan said. "I have to prepare lunch boxes for the entire household, and am I wailing? And Haobo and Mugang and all the men have to prepare the sedan chairs and get ready to carry fat FuDing for hours tomorrow, and they aren't crying, either. So your sniveling is not welcome!"

I gulped and rubbed my face with my sleeve. "Why are we getting lunch boxes and sedan chairs ready?" I asked. "Where is the family going?"

"Where are we all going, you mean," Bisi said. "They're taking all of us this time—even you."

"Me?" I asked, surprised. I had assumed that Mrs. Li and the family were going on an extravagant picnic or visiting Aunt Xue or some other rich cousins' mansion. "Where? Why?"

"It's the first of the month, stupid!" Bisi said. "You may have gotten all those fancy lessons and learned to read, but you're still not very smart. They are taking us to the temple service, of course."

"But the Temple of Longevity is not hours—" I began.

"We're not going to the Temple of Longevity," Bisi said with exasperation, but I could see that her frustration was more about the inconvenience than it was for me. "We're off to the Infinite Stream Temple this time."

"That huge gold temple by the ocean?" I said. "Why?"

"For FuDing, of course," Shuwan said. "Mrs. Li hopes she can get the abbot to be a matchmaker for him. Infinite

Stream Temple! That's why it has so much money—it gets an infinite stream of bribes."

"She'll need an elephant's weight of gold to get a matchmaker for FuDing," Bisi grunted. "No matchmaker is going to arrange a marriage with a well-born girl to that rice bucket. You'd think Mrs. Li would know that."

"She does. Mrs. Li is no fool! Why do you think—" Shuwan stopped, and both servants looked at me oddly.

"What?" I asked. As the silence grew longer, I put down the teapot I was washing and glared at them. "What?" I demanded. "Tell me!"

"By the time FuDing was seven, everyone knew he was a brute as well as an idiot," Shuwan said. "And Mrs. Li knew that he might have a hard time finding a bride . . . ."

"Why do you think Mrs. Li was so desperate for you, the granddaughter of a scholar?" Bisi said. "She could've gotten any peasant's kid for cheaper and without any silly promises. She wanted a girl of good blood, just in case."

I stared. If Mrs. Li couldn't find a suitable bride, I was going to have to marry FuDing? Me? I felt as if I had eaten spoiled fish.

"You're not marrying age yet," Shuwan said, trying to be kind. "You have a couple of years. That's why Mrs. Li is trying to find FuDing a bride now. She's hoping she can get someone else to marry FuDing before you have to."

"Though I'd say that's a pretty bleak hope!" Bisi sniffed.

I thought of FuDing and his hairy fingers that were too clumsy to hold a paintbrush but so adept at torturing bugs. If I had listened more carefully, would I have heard their silent screams? Tears of horror filled my eyes.

Shuwan heaved an impatient sigh. "You made her cry again!" she complained.

"Well," Bisi retorted, "at least this time she's got a good reason."

The next morning, the streets around the House of Li overflowed with servants, horses, and sedan chairs. Mrs. Li's chair was so large that it needed four men on either side to carry it. FuDing's was not as large, but he was so heavy that the same number of men were needed to carry him. Then the cousins and aunts filled the carriages, and the horses were burdened with the supplies and gifts. Shuwan, Bisi, and I were to share a donkey, with the agreement that we would take turns riding, even though I had doubts about when my turn would be.

"It's sheer craziness!" Shuwan grumbled as we paraded past the **gawking** neighbors, most of them awed by the grandness of our procession. "Going to that ocean temple carrying chests of jade and strings of cash! We'll be prime targets for robbers. I wouldn't be surprised if pirates docked their boats just to raid us."

....

gawking openly staring

I remembered Shuwan's fear of pirates.

"Weren't some pirates seen recently?" I asked slyly. "I think someone said it was the Red Flag Fleet."

"I hope not!" Shuwan said with such fear that I felt a little bad for teasing her. "They are the worst! No one can stop the Red Flag Fleet!"

"The Imperial Navy has tried three times to capture them," Bisi said helpfully, "but failed each time. I heard that the Emperor has even offered amnesty to the captain and the crew if they'd agree to retire."

"Why would they retire?" Shuwan said. "They take what they want, and no one can stop them. And here we're going with all our gold! We might as well be throwing it into the ocean for them."

The trip to Infinite Stream Temple was a long one, but enjoyable. My turn to ride the donkey came much sooner than I had expected, for my short legs could not keep up with the procession, and Shuwan was ordered to allow me to ride so that I wouldn't slow down the group. She did this **begrudgingly**, until it was discovered that because I was so small, the donkey could bear the weight of another. So I rode along merrily, enjoying Shuwan and Bisi's bickering about who would ride with me.

And I marveled at all I saw. Even the scrubby, unkempt brush on the dirt road was a pleasure to see. Mrs. Li insisted

....

begrudgingly with resentment

that her residence be immaculate at all times. Even stray leaves had to be plucked from the paths of the garden. (I knew this because clearing the walkways was one of my jobs.)

But the sea was what **mesmerized** me. It whispered with a quiet thunder, and when I saw the "waves made of dragon scales," just like in one of Li Po's poems, I gasped.

However, after "thirty-six twists and turns of the valley," the Infinite Stream Temple came into view. High on a rocky hill, it was impossible to miss, for even from a distance the temple was a brilliance of gold. The temple's bright yellow and red walls and roofs dazzled, a loud, vibrating blare among the soft grays and silvers of the landscape.

"If I were a pirate," I said, ''I'd raid that temple myself."

"Shut up about pirates already!" Shuwan snapped.

I grinned and our procession began along the path toward the temple. As the donkey climbed I heard the murmur of the sea, as if it were sighing a secret, and turned to look down at it. From my seat on the donkey, I could see the expanse of the ocean—the rolling waves glistening like silver folds of silk embroidered with threads of… red? I straightened. Unmoving and still, a dozen large junks sat in the water, the masts red-wrapped spikes stabbing into the sky, as if waiting. Waiting for what? Their captain and crew? But the only seamen who would dare raise a crimson

<hr />

mesmerized spellbound, fascinated

sail were the Red Flag Fleet pirates! I scanned the shoreline below and stared at the **sampans**—fifty of them, or maybe even a hundred, all piled together like discarded shoes in the sand. As one stray sampan began to bob away, I felt my own thoughts lurch. There were pirates here!

"Bisi," I said, grabbing her arm. "Pirates!"

"Stop teasing Shuwan." Bisi shook me off. "You little brat, you think you're so funny …."

But her voice trailed off as hundreds of screams echoed from the front of the procession. Servants, silk, and sedans seemed to fly toward me, and I felt Bisi throw herself from the donkey, shoving me face-first onto the ground. Something hard hit the back of my head, but before all became black, I knew that the Li family had reached the doors of the temple and had been welcomed in by the pirates.

I dreamed I was a small child, being rocked gently in a mother's arms. "Shhh," she whispered in my ear. "Shhh …."

"Is that one awake yet?" a rough voice said.

My eyes flew open. The soft rocking had been caused by the waves of the sea, and the ocean's roar had been the whisper. I sat up and saw a splash of red against blue—an unfurled sail against the sky. I was on a pirate boat!

"Now she is!" another voice hooted.

....

sampans boats that have a flat bottom

A forest of men stood before me, but beneath the raucous laughter, I heard sniffling. I looked and saw Bisi next to me, whimpering like a puppy.

"This was supposed to be a grab-and-go!" a man said. "The captain's not going to like seeing these prisoners."

"Indeed," a low voice behind me said as all the men immediately quieted. "She does not."

The captain was a woman? She strode forward, and it was then that I saw Tianyi, the captain of the Red Flag Fleet, the most feared pirate of the sea.

I could only gape. Teacher had once told me about the powerful goddess Xi Wangmu and how she was sometimes described as ferocious and terrible, having the claws and teeth of a tiger and the tail of a panther. But she was also described as being incredibly lovely and the Queen of the Heavens. I had protested at the conflicting descriptions. I had thought it impossible for one to be so beautiful and so fierce at the same time, but as I gazed at Tianyi, I suddenly understood. Her black silk hair billowed like the sails behind her, and her eyes sparkled like black coals ready to flame.

"Well, Weigu?" Tianyi said, and I saw the pirate actually whiten.

"I thought maybe that one could be ransomed," the pirate named Weigu replied, nodding toward me. "That family had a child, right? I thought maybe this one was it."

Tianyi gave me a quick glance and made a sound of annoyance.

"Stupid donkey! Look at her! Are those the clothes of someone from a rich family?" she said. She grabbed my hands and thrust them in the pirate's face. "Look at these hands! These are the hands of a servant! There's no ransom here! Idiot!"

The pirate cowered as Tianyi looked around. "And what straw bag grabbed her?" she said, nodding toward Bisi.

"Dihan took her," one of the men said. "He thought she was pretty."

"Did he?" Tianyi said dangerously. She drew her sword and walked to a man, placing her sword at his neck. "If you tried to spoil her, I'll cut your head off."

"I didn't!" the man protested. "I promise!"

"I know," Tianyi said with a sweet smile, putting her sword away. "That's why I'm not going to."

"I thought...you know how the Po Tsai pirates asked us for a woman to trade, and we owe them for that fight with the Imperial Navy when our other ships were late and... and...," Dihan began to stammer.

Tianyi looked at Bisi—even with her nose red from crying she did look rather nice—and contemplated. For a brief moment, I saw Tianyi's eyes flash with pity.

"Too plain," Tianyi said, looking away. She tossed her hand. "They won't want her."

"Too plain?" Dihan asked. "That's what you said last time!"

"Do you think I cannot judge a woman's beauty?" Tianyi said, taking a step toward him. Like Weigu, Dihan cringed. "Give them enough cash to return and we'll drop them off at the next port." Then, throwing Dihan a cold glance, she added, "Perhaps we should have your wife help you bring them to shore."

"Please!" I was shocked to hear my own voice. "Don't send me back."

Everyone looked at me in astonishment, and I could not blame them. But even though the words had spilled out of me without thought, I suddenly found that I truly meant them. What did I have to return to? Being bossed by everyone, scrubbing chamber pots, and marrying FuDing? I shuddered at the thought.

But Tianyi had already dismissed me. "This is a pirate ship, not a nursery," she said. Then, addressing the crew, she ordered, "Bring up the rest of the loot!"

I bowed my head, surprised by the tears that filled my eyes. Bisi hissed a stream of insults at me, which, after years of practice, I easily ignored. Instead, after wiping my eyes, I found myself fascinated as the men threw the chests and packages from the sampans in such a well-practiced rhythm that it seemed to match the movement of the waves.

But not perfect. "Hey! Dumb melon!" shouted a pirate as another fumbled with a crate of tea bricks. It splashed into the water.

"Ohh!" I groaned. "And that was Iron Goddess tea!"

I had spoken aloud, thinking no one was listening to me. But Tianyi had the ears of a tiger and turned at my words. "How do you know that was Iron Goddess tea?" she demanded.

"It said so," I answered. "On the label."

"And this batch here," she said, pointing to another tea brick. "Is this Iron Goddess, too?"

"No," I said. "It says 'Mountain Silver Needle tea.'"

Tianyi tore open the package, broke off some leaves in her hands, and smelled the tea. She looked at me carefully, her eyes piercing. "Come with me," she ordered.

She led me into the captain's quarters, where I gazed around with great interest. It was a room of luxury—lavish silks draped over plush cushions, an intricately carved sandalwood bed, and red lanterns. In the entrance, two small wooden soldiers stood guard in front of a shrine that housed a goddess carved of ivory, surrounded by marigolds. Tianyi motioned me to sit, and I watched curiously as she pulled out a wooden chest, plain and uncarved.

"Long ago, we raided a passenger ship. While all the wealthy nobles threw their goods at us and begged for mercy, one man jumped in front of this chest and grabbed a sword," Tianyi said. "He held the sword as if it were a broomstick, and it was easy to see he was no match for even the smallest of my men. But he fought valiantly to protect his treasure." Her face softened at the memory.

"I would have spared him for that, but he was mortally wounded."

Tianyi worked the chest's clasp as she continued. "As he fought, I wondered what treasure he had that was so valuable. And when he died, I found it was this."

She opened the chest and I gasped. Books! Hundreds of books! I put my hands on them reverently. *Poems of Li Po. The Classic of Music. Spring and Autumn Annals.*

"Can you read these?" Tianyi asked me. I nodded.

She looked at me, her eyes sparkling with an inner fire. "Teach me," she said, "and you can stay."

So I did.

* * *

Now, as I write this on a pirate ship whose red sails paint the sky, I ride the vast ocean. The wind is wild, and the waves are endless, and the shore is so distant it is hard to imagine that it even exists. But my head is raised and I can't help but smile. For while the path before me might be difficult, it will be my own. ❖

Primary Lessons

from Silent Dancing: A Partial Remembrance
of a Puerto Rican Childhood
by Judith Ortiz Cofer

My mother walked me to my first day at school at La
Escuela Segundo Ruiz Belvis, named after the Puerto Rican
patriot born in our town. I remember yellow cement with
green trim. All the classrooms had been painted these
colors to identify them as government property. This
was true all over the Island. Everything was color coded,
including the children, who wore uniforms from first
through twelfth grade. We were a midget army in white
and brown, led by the hand to our battleground. From
practically every house in our **barrio** emerged a crisply
ironed uniform inhabited by the savage creatures we had
become over a summer of running wild in the sun.

barrio neighborhood

At my grandmother's house where we were staying until my father returned to Brooklyn Yard in New York and sent for us, it had been complete chaos, with several children to get ready for school. My mother had pulled my hair harder than usual while braiding it, and I had dissolved into a pool of total self-pity. I wanted to stay home with her and Mamá, to continue listening to stories in the late afternoon, to drink *café con leche* with them, and to play rough games with my many cousins. I wanted to continue living the dream of summer afternoons in Puerto Rico, and if I could not have it, then I wanted to go back to Paterson, New Jersey, back to where I imagined our apartment waited, peaceful and cool, for the three of us to return to our former lives. Our gypsy lifestyle had convinced me, at age six, that one part of life stops and waits for you while you live another for a while—and if you don't like the present, you can always return to the past. Buttoning me into my stiff blouse while I tried to squirm away from her, my mother attempted to explain to me that I was a big girl now and should try to understand that, like all the other children my age, I had to go to school.

"What about him?" I yelled, pointing at my brother who was lounging on the tile floor of our bedroom in his pajamas, playing quietly with a toy car.

"He's too young to go to school, you know that. Now stay still." My mother pinned me between her thighs to

---

café con leche coffee with milk

button my skirt, as she had learned to do from Mamá, from whose grip it was impossible to escape.

"It's not fair, it's not fair. I can't go to school here. I don't speak Spanish." It was my final argument, and it failed miserably because I was shouting my defiance in the language I claimed not to speak. Only I knew what I meant by saying in Spanish that I did not speak Spanish. I had spent my early childhood in the U.S. where I lived in a bubble created by my Puerto Rican parents in a home where two cultures and languages became one. I learned to listen to the English from the television with one ear while I heard my mother and father speaking in Spanish with the other. I thought I was an ordinary American kid—like the children on the shows I watched—and that everyone's parents spoke a secret second language at home. When we came to Puerto Rico right before I started first grade, I switched easily to Spanish. It was the language of fun, of summertime games. But school—that was a different matter.

I made one last desperate effort to make my mother see reason: "Father will be very angry. You know that he wants us to speak good English." My mother, of course, ignored me as she dressed my little brother in his playclothes. I could not believe her indifference to my father's wishes. She was usually so careful about our safety and the many other areas that he was forever reminding her about in his letters. But I was right, and she knew it. Our father spoke to us in English as much as possible, and he corrected my pronunciation constantly—not "jes" but "y-es." Y-es, sir. How could she send me to school to learn Spanish when we would be returning to Paterson in just a few months?

But, of course, what I feared was not language, but loss of freedom. At school there would be no playing, no stories, only lessons. It would not matter if I did not understand a word, and I would not be allowed to make up my own definitions. I would have to learn silence. I would have to keep my wild imagination in check. Feeling locked into my stiffly starched uniform, I only sensed all this. I guess most children can **intuit** their loss of childhood's freedom on that first day of school. It is separation anxiety too, but mother is just the guardian of the "playground" of our early childhood.

The sight of my cousins in similar straits comforted me. We were marched down the hill of our barrio where Mamá's robin-egg-blue house stood at the top. I must have glanced back at it with yearning. Mamá's house—a place built for children—where anything that could be broken had already been broken by my grandmother's early batch of offspring (they ranged in age from my mother's oldest sisters to my uncle who was six months older than me). Her house had long since been made child-proof. It had been a perfect summer place. And now it was September—the cruelest month for a child. ❖

---

intuit to sense or know by instinct

How a Cat Played Robinson Crusoe

by Charles G. D. Roberts

I

The island was a mere sandbank off the low, flat coast.
Not a tree broke its **bleak** levels—not even a shrub. But the
long, gritty stalks of the marsh grass clothed it everywhere
above tide mark, and a tiny **rivulet** of sweet water, flowing
from a spring at its center, drew a ribbon of green across
the harsh and **somber** yellow gray of the grass.

---

bleak grim
rivulet a small river or stream
somber serious

Few would have chosen the island as a place to live. Yet at its seaward end, where the changing tides were never still, stood a cottage, with a low shed behind it. When the mainland would be **sweltering** day and night, on the island there was always a cool wind blowing. And on this cool plot of sand, a wise city dweller had built his summer home.

The family came to the island toward the end of June. In the first week of September they went away, leaving every door and window of the house and shed securely shuttered, bolted, or barred against the winter's storms. A roomy boat, rowed by two fishermen, carried them across the half mile of racing tides that separated them from the mainland.

After two months of wind, sun, waves, and waving grass tops, the elders of the household were not sorry to get back to the world. But the children went with tear-stained faces. They were leaving behind them their favorite pet, a handsome, moonfaced cat, striped like a tiger. The animal had disappeared two days before, without leaving a trace behind. The only reasonable explanation seemed to be that she had been snapped up by a passing eagle. The cat, meanwhile, was a prisoner at the other end of the island, hidden beneath a broken barrel and drifted sand.

---

sweltering unbearably hot

The old barrel, with the **staves** battered out of one side, had stood, half buried, on the crest of a sand ridge raised by a steady wind. Under it the cat had found a sheltered hollow, full of sun, where she liked to lie curled up for hours at a time, **basking** and sleeping. Meanwhile the sand had been steadily piling itself higher and higher behind the unstable barrier. At last it had piled too high, and suddenly, in response to a stronger gust, the barrel had come toppling over beneath a mass of sand, burying the sleeping cat out of sight and light. But at the same time the sound half of the barrel had formed a safe roof to her prison, and she was neither crushed nor smothered.

When the children in their anxious search all over the island chanced upon the mound of fine, white sand, they gave it but one careless look. They could not hear the faint cries that came, at intervals, from the darkness within. So they went away sorrow fully, little dreaming that their friend was imprisoned almost beneath their feet.

For three days the prisoner kept up her appeals for help. On the third day the wind changed and blew up a gale. In a few hours it had uncovered the barrel. At one corner a tiny spot of light appeared.

Eagerly the cat stuck her paw through the hole. When she withdrew it again the hole was much larger. She

---

staves strips of wood that form the sides of a barrel
basking lying in and enjoying the warmth of the sun

took the hint and fell to scratching. At first her efforts were rather **aimless**, but soon, whether by good luck or cleverness, she learned to make her scratching more effective. The opening rapidly enlarged, and at last she was able to squeeze her way out.

Filled with flying sand, the wind was tearing madly across the island. The seas hurled themselves trampling up the beach, with the uproar of a **bombardment**. The grasses lay bowed flat in long, quivering ranks. Over the turmoil the sun stared down from a deep, unclouded blue. The cat, when she first met the full force of the gale, was fairly blown off her feet. As soon as she could recover, she crouched low and darted for shelter. She sped straight before the gale, making for the cottage where she fondly imagined she would find not only food and shelter, but also loving comfort to make her forget her terrors.

Still and desolate in the bright sunshine and the tearing wind, the house frightened her. She could not understand the tight-closed shutters, or the blind, unresponding doors that would no longer open to her anxious appeal. The wind swept her **savagely** across the **veranda**. Climbing with difficulty to the dining room window sill, where so often she had been let in, she clung there a few moments

....

aimless without direction
bombardment an attack, as with cannons or bombs
savagely fiercely
veranda a porch

and yowled heartbrokenly. Then, in a sudden panic, she jumped down and ran to the shed. That, too, was closed. Never before had she seen the shed doors closed, and she could not understand it. Cautiously she crept around the foundations—but there was no getting in that way. On every side it was nothing but a blank, forbidding face that the old familiar house **confronted** her with.

The cat had always been so **coddled** and pampered by the children that she had had no need to **forage** for herself. Fortunately for her, she had learned to hunt the marsh mice and grass spar rows for amusement. So now, **ravenous** from her long fast under the sand, she slunk mournfully away from the deserted house and crept along under the lee of a sand ridge to a little grassy hollow.

Here the gale caught only the tops of the grasses. And here, in the warmth and comparative calm, the mice and shrews were going about their business undisturbed. The cat, quick and stealthy, soon caught one and eased her hunger. She caught several. And then, making her way back to the house, she spent hours in heartsick prowling, sniffing and peering, yowling piteously on threshold and windowsill. At last, hopelessly discouraged, she curled herself up beneath the children's window and went to sleep.

....

confronted challenged
coddled spoiled
forage to search for food
ravenous extremely hungry

II

In spite of her loneliness and grief, the life of the island prisoner during the next two or three weeks was by no means one of hardship. Be sides her abundant food of birds and mice, she quickly learned to catch tiny fish in the mouth of the rivulet, where salt water and fresh water met. It was an exciting game, and she became expert at dashing the gray tomcod and blue-and-silver sand lance far up the slope with a sweep of her armed paw.

But when the storms roared down upon the island, with furious rain, and low, black clouds torn to shreds, then life became more difficult for her. Game all took to cover, where it was hard to find. It was difficult to get around in the drenched and **lashing** grass, and she **loathed** being wet. Most of the time she went hungry, sitting **sullen** and **desolate** under the lee of the house, glaring out defiantly at the battling **tumult** of the waves.

The storm lasted nearly ten days. On the eighth day the abandoned wreck of a small schooner drove ashore. The battered hulk had passengers of a sort. A horde of rats got through the surf and scurried into the grass roots. They promptly made themselves at home, burrowing under the

....

lashing moving in a violent, whip-like way
loathed hated
sullen sulky, gloomy
desolate very lonely and joyless
tumult commotion

dead grass, and carrying panic into the ranks of the mice and shrews.

When the storm was over, the cat had a surprise in her first long hunting expedition. Something had rustled the grass heavily, and she trailed it, expecting a particularly large, fat marsh mouse. When she pounced upon an immense old ship's rat, she got badly bitten. Such an experience had never before happened to her. At first she felt so injured that she was on the point of backing out and running away. Then the fire of far-off ancestors awoke within her. She flung herself furiously into the fight, and the struggle was soon over. Her wounds, faithfully licked, quickly healed in that clean and healthy air. After that, having learned how to handle such big game, she got bitten no more.

During the first full moon after her abandonment—the first week in October—the island was visited by still weather with sharp night frosts. The cat discovered then that it was most exciting to hunt by night and do her sleeping in the daytime. She found that now, under the strange whiteness of the moon, all her game was astir—except the birds, which had fled to the mainland during the storm, gathering for the southward flight. Everywhere the blanched grasses rustled, and everywhere dim little shapes went darting with thin squeaks across ghostly white sands. Also she made the acquaintance of a new bird, which she regarded at first uneasily and then with **vengeful** wrath. This was the brown marsh owl, which came over from the mainland to do some autumn mouse hunting. There were two pairs of these big, downy-winged, round-eyed hunters, and they did not know there was a cat on the island.

The cat, spying one of them as it swooped soundlessly over the silvered grass, crouched with flattened ears. With its wide spread of wing and its great round face with hooked beak and wild, staring eyes, it appeared very threatening. However, she was no coward; and soon, she went about her hunting, though cautiously. Suddenly, the owl caught a partial glimpse of her ears in the grass. He swooped, and at the same instant she sprang upward to meet the assault, spitting and growling harshly, and striking with unsheathed claws. With a frantic flapping of his great wings the owl checked him self and drew back into the air. After that the marsh owls realized that it was best not to interfere with the black-striped animal with the quick spring and the clutching claws.

III

Winter deepened, with bursts of sharp cold and changing winds that forced the cat continually to seek new **refuge**. She grew more and more unhappy, and felt her

---

vengeful seeking revenge; eager to get even or get back at
refuge a safe place

homelessness **keenly**. Nowhere on the whole island could she find a nook where she might feel secure from both wind and rain. As for the old barrel, the first cause of her misfortunes, there was no help in that. The winds had long ago turned it com pletely over, open to the sky, then drifted it full of sand and reburied it. And in any case, the cat would have been afraid to go near it again.

So it came about that she alone of all the island dwellers had no shelter when the real winter arrived, with snows that smothered the grass tops out of sight, and frosts that lined the shore with grinding ice cakes. The rats had their holes under the buried fragments of wreckage; the mice and shrews had their deep, warm tunnels; the owls had nests in hollow trees far away in the forests of the mainland. But the cat, shivering and frightened, could do nothing but crouch against the blind walls of the unrelenting house and let the snow whirl itself about her.

And now, in her misery, she found her food cut off. The mice ran secure in their hidden runways, where the grass roots on each side gave them easy and abundant food. The rats, too, were out of sight, digging burrows in the soft snow. The ice fringe, crumbling and heaving under the ruthless tide, put an end to her fishing. She would have tried to capture one of the **formidable** owls in her hunger,

....

keenly sharply
formidable inspiring awe, wonder, or fear

but the owls no longer came to the island, as they were following an easier chase in the deeps of the upland forest.

When the snow stopped and the sun came out again, there fell such keen cold as the cat had never felt before. The day, as it chanced, was Christmas; and if the cat had had any idea of the calendar she would certainly have marked the day in her memory, as it proved to be an important one for her.

Starving as she was, she could not sleep, but kept ceaselessly on the prowl. This was fortunate, for had she gone to sleep with no more shelter than the wall of the house, she would never have awakened again. In her restlessness she wandered to the farther side of the island where, in a sunny recess of the shore facing the mainland, she found a patch of bare sand, free of ice cakes and just uncovered by the tide. Opening upon this recess were the tiny entrances to several of the mouse tunnels.

Close beside one of these holes in the snow the cat crouched, quivering, **intent**. For ten minutes or more she waited, never so much as twitching a whisker. At last a mouse thrust out its little pointed head. Not daring to give it time to change its mind or take alarm, she pounced. The mouse doubled back into the narrow runway. Hardly realizing what she did in her desperation, the cat plunged head and shoulders into the snow, reaching blindly after

....
intent focused on some purpose

the vanished prize. By great good luck she caught it. It was her first meal in four bitter days.

Now she had learned a lesson. Being naturally clever, and her wits being sharpened by fierce necessity, she understood that it was possible to follow her prey a little way into the snow. Since she had wiped out the door of this particular runway, she went and crouched beside a similar one, but here she had to wait a long time before an adventurous mouse came to peer out. But this time she showed that she had learned her lesson. She pounced straight at the side of the entrance, where instinct told her that the body of the mouse would be. One outstretched paw thus cut off the **quarry's** retreat. Her tactics were successful—as her head went plunging into the fluffy whiteness, she felt the prize between her paws.

Her hunger **appeased**, she found herself immensely excited over this new way of hunting. Often before had she waited at mouse holes, but never had she found it possible to break down the walls and invade the holes themselves. It was a thrilling idea. As she crept toward another hole a mouse scurried swiftly up the sand and darted into it. The cat, too late to catch him before he disappeared, tried to follow him. Scratching clumsily but hopefully, she succeeded in forcing the full length of her body into the

....

quarry prey; an animal hunted or chased
appeased calmed; soothed; satisfied

snow. She found no sign of the fugitive, which was by this time racing in safety down some dim tunnel. With her eyes, mouth, whiskers, and fur full of powdery white particles, she backed out, much disappointed. But in that moment she realized it was much warmer in there beneath the snow than out in the stinging air. It was a second vitally important lesson that she instinctively put into practice a little while later.

IV

She caught yet another mouse and carried it back to the house. She laid it down in tribute on the veranda steps while she meowed and stared hopefully at the desolate, snow-draped door. Getting no response, she carried the mouse down to the hollow behind a drift caused by the bulging bay window on the end of the house. Here she curled herself up forlornly, thinking to have a wink of sleep.

But the still cold was too biting. She looked at the sloping wall of snow beside her and cautiously thrust her paw into it. It was very soft and light. It seemed to offer very little resistance. She pawed away in an awkward fashion till she had scooped out a sort of tiny cave. Gently she pushed herself into it, pressing back the snow on every side till she had room to turn around. Then turn around she did several times, as dogs do in getting their beds arranged to their liking.

In this way she not only packed down the snow beneath her, but she also rounded out for her self a snug chamber with a narrow doorway. From this snowy retreat she gazed forth with a solemn air of possession; then she went to sleep with a sense of comfort, of "homeyness," such as she had never before felt since the disappearance of her friends.

From now on, her life in the winter wild, though **strenuous**, was no longer one of any terrible hardship. With patience at the mouse holes she could catch enough to eat. In her snowy den she slept warm and secure. In a little while, when a crust had formed over the surface of the snow, the mice took to coming out at night. Then the owls, too, came back. The cat tried to catch one, but got sharply bitten and clawed before she let it go. After this she decided that owls were meant to be let alone. But still she enjoyed fine hunting out there on the bleak, white reaches of the snow.

When spring came back to the island, with the nightly shrill chorus of frogs in the shallow pools, and the young grass alive with nesting birds, the prisoner's life became almost pleasant in its easy abundance. But now she was once more homeless, since her snug den had vanished with the snow. This did not much matter, however, for the weather grew warmer and more tranquil day by day. And she herself, in being forced back upon her instincts,

strenuous requiring great effort

had learned to be contented. Nevertheless, with all her capacity for learning and adapting herself, she had not forgotten anything.

One day in June, a crowded boat arrived from the mainland, and children's voices came clamoring across the grass tops, breaking the desolate silence of the island. The cat heard and sprang up out of her sleep on the veranda steps.

For one second she stood, listening intently. Then, almost as a dog would do, and as few of her tribe ever **condescend** to do, she went racing across to the landing place—to be snatched up into the arms of four happy children at once, and to have her fine fur ruffled to a state that would cost her an hour's careful grooming to put in order. ❖

---

condescend to lower oneself

Tears of Autumn

by Yoshiko Uchida

Hana Omiya stood at the railing of the small ship that shuddered toward America in a turbulent November sea. She shivered as she pulled the folds of her silk **kimono** close to her throat and tightened the wool shawl about her shoulders.

She was thin and small, her dark eyes shadowed in her pale face, her black hair piled high in a **pompadour** that seemed too heavy for so slight a woman. She clung to the moist rail and breathed the damp salt air deep into her lungs. Her body seemed leaden and lifeless, as though it were simply the vehicle transporting her soul to a strange new life, and she longed with childlike intensity to be home again in Oka Village.

She longed to see the bright **persimmon** dotting the barren trees beside the thatched roots, to see the fields of golden rice stretching to the mountains where only last fall she had gathered plump white mushrooms, and to see once more the maple trees lacing their flaming colors through the green pine. If only she could see a familiar face, eat a meal without retching, walk on solid ground, and stretch

----

kimono a wide-sleeved Japanese robe
pompadour a hairstyle worn high over the forehead
persimmon a small orange tree fruit

out at night on a **tatami mat** instead of in a hard narrow bunk. She thought now of seeking the warm shelter of her bunk but could not bear to face the relentless smell of fish that penetrated the lower decks.

Why did I ever leave Japan? she wondered bitterly. Why did I ever listen to my uncle? And yet she knew it was she herself who had begun the chain of events that placed her on this heaving ship. It was she who had first planted in her uncle the thought that she would make a good wife for Taro, the lonely man who had gone to America to make his home in Oakland, California.

It all began one day when her uncle had come to visit her mother.

"I must find a nice young bride," he had said, startling Hana with this blunt talk of marriage in her presence. She blushed and was ready to leave the room when her uncle quickly added, "My good friend Takeda has a son in America. I must find someone willing to travel to that far land."

This last remark was intended to indicate to Hana and her mother that he didn't consider this a suitable prospect for Hana, who was the youngest daughter of what once had been a fine family. Her father, until his death fifteen years ago, had been the largest landholder of the village and one of its last **samurai**. They had once had many

tatami mat a traditional Japanese straw mat used as floor covering
samurai a member of the powerful, historic Japanese warrior class

servants and field hands, but now all that was changed. Their money was gone. Hana's three older sisters had made good marriages, and the eldest remained in their home with her husband to carry on the Omiya name and perpetuate the homestead. Her other sisters had married merchants in Osaka and Nagoya and were living comfortably.

Now that Hana was twenty-one, finding a proper husband for her had taken on an urgency that produced an embarrassing secretive air over the entire matter. Usually, her mother didn't speak of it until they were lying side by side on their quilts at night. Then, under the protective cover of darkness, she would suggest one name and then another, hoping that Hana would indicate an interest in one of them.

Her uncle spoke freely of Taro Takeda only because he was so sure Hana would never consider him. "He is a conscientious, hardworking man who has been in the United States for almost ten years. He is thirty-one, operates a small shop, and rents some rooms above the shop where he lives." Her uncle rubbed his chin thoughtfully. "He could provide well for a wife," he added.

"Ah," Hana's mother said softly.

"You say he is successful in this business?" Hana's sister inquired.

"His father tells me he sells many things in his shop— clothing, stockings, needles, thread, and buttons—such things as that. He also sells bean paste, pickled radish, bean cake, and soy sauce. A wife of his, would not go cold or hungry."

They all nodded, each of them picturing this merchant in varying degrees of success and affluence. There were many Japanese emigrating to America these days, and Hana had heard of the picture brides who went with nothing more than an exchange of photographs to bind them to a strange man.

"Taro San is lonely," her uncle continued. "I want to find for him a fine young woman who is strong and brave enough to cross the ocean alone."

"It would certainly be a different kind of life," Hana's sister ventured, and for a moment, Hana thought she glimpsed a longing ordinarily concealed behind her quiet, obedient face. In that same instant, Hana knew she wanted more for herself than her sisters had in their proper, arranged, and loveless marriages. She wanted to escape the smothering **strictures** of life in her village. She certainly was not going to marry a farmer and spend her life working beside him planting, weeding, and harvesting in the rice paddies until her back became bent from too many years of stooping and her skin was turned to brown leather by the sun and wind. Neither did she particularly relish the idea of marrying a merchant in a big city as her two sisters had done. Since her mother objected to her going to

----

strictures limits on behavior or activities

Tokyo to seek employment as a teacher, perhaps she would consent to a flight to America for what seemed a proper and respectable marriage.

Almost before she realized what she was doing, she spoke to her uncle. "Oji San, perhaps I should go to America to make this lonely man a good wife."

"You, Hana Chan?" Her uncle observed her with startled curiosity. "You would go all alone to a foreign land so far away from your mother and family?"

"I would not allow it." Her mother spoke fiercely. Hana was her youngest and she had lavished upon her the attention and latitude that often befall the last child. How could she permit her to travel so far, even to marry the son of Takeda who was known to her brother?

But now, a notion that had seemed quite impossible a moment before was lodged in his receptive mind, and Hana's uncle grasped it with the pleasure that comes from an unexpected discovery.

"You know," he said looking at Hana, "it might be a very good life in America."

Hana felt a faint fluttering in her heart. Perhaps this lonely man in America was her means of escaping both the village and the encirclement of her family.

Her uncle spoke with increasing enthusiasm of sending Hana to become Taro's wife. And the husband of Hana's sister, who was head of their household, spoke with equal eagerness. Although he never said so, Hana guessed he would be pleased to be rid of her, the spirited younger sister who stirred up his placid life with what he considered radical ideas about life and the role of women. He often claimed that Hana had too much schooling for a girl. She had graduated from Women's High School in Kyoto, which gave her five more years of schooling than her older sister.

"It has addled her brain—all that learning from those books," he said when he tired of arguing with Hana.

A man's word carried much weight for Hana's mother. Pressed by the two men, she consulted her other daughters and their husbands. She discussed the matter carefully with her brother and asked the village priest. Finally, she agreed to an exchange of family histories and an investigation was begun into Taro Takeda's family, his education, and his health, so they would be assured there was no insanity or tuberculosis or police records concealed in his family's past. Soon Hana's uncle was devoting his energies entirely to serving as go-between for Hana's mother and Taro Takeda's father.

When at last an agreement to the marriage was almost reached, Taro wrote his first letter to Hana. It was brief and proper and gave no more clue to his character than the stiff formal portrait taken at his graduation from middle school. Hana's uncle had given her the picture with apologies from his parents, because it was the only photo they had of him and it was not a flattering likeness.

Hana hid the letter and photograph in the sleeve of her kimono and took them to the outhouse to study in private. Squinting in the dim light and trying to ignore the foul odor, she read and reread Taro's letter, trying to find the real man somewhere in the sparse unbending prose.

By the time he sent her money for her steamship tickets, she had received ten more letters, but none revealed much more of the man than the first. In none did he disclose his loneliness or his need, but Hana understood this. In fact, she would have recoiled from a man who bared his intimate thoughts to her so soon. After all, they would have a lifetime together to get to know each other.

So it was that Hana had left her family and sailed alone to America with a small hope trembling inside of her. Tomorrow at last, the ship would dock in San Francisco and she would meet face to face the man she was soon to marry. Hana was overcome with excitement at the thought of being in America, and terrified of the meeting about to take place. What would she say to Taro Takeda when they first met, and for all the days and years after?

Hana wondered about the flat above the shop. Perhaps it would be luxuriously furnished with the finest of brocades and lacquers, and perhaps there would be a servant, although he had not mentioned it. She worried whether she would be able to manage on the meager English she had learned at Women's High School. The overwhelming anxiety for the day to come and the violent rolling of the ship were more than Hana could bear. Shuddering in the face of the wind, she leaned over the railing and became violently and wretchedly ill.

By five the next morning, Hana was up and dressed in her finest purple silk kimono and coat. She could not eat the bean soup and rice that appeared for breakfast and took only a few bites of the yellow pickled radish. Her bags, which had scarcely been touched since she boarded the ship, were easily packed, for all they contained were her kimonos and some of her favorite books. The large willow basket, tightly secured by a rope, remained under the bunk, untouched since her uncle had placed it there.

She had not befriended the other women in her cabin, for they had lain in their bunks for most of the voyage, too sick to be company to anyone. Each morning Hana had fled the closeness of the sleeping quarters and spent most of the day huddled in a corner of the deck, listening to the lonely songs of some Russians also traveling to an alien land.

As the ship approached land, Hana hurried up to the deck to look out at the gray expanse of ocean and sky, eager for a first glimpse of her new homeland.

"We won't be docking until almost noon," one of the deckhands told her.

Hana nodded, "I can wait," she answered, but the last hours seemed the longest.

When she set foot on American soil at last, it was not in the city of San Francisco as she had expected, but on Angel Island, where all third-class passengers were taken. She spent two miserable days and nights waiting, as the immigrants were questioned by officials, examined for trachoma and tuberculosis, and tested for hookworm by a woman who collected their stools on tin pie plates. Hana was relieved she could produce her own, not having to borrow a little from someone else, as some of the women had to do. It was a bewildering, degrading beginning, and Hana was sick with anxiety, wondering if she would ever be released.

On the third day, a Japanese messenger from San Francisco appeared with a letter for her from Taro. He had written it the day of her arrival, but it had not reached her for two days.

Taro welcomed her to America, and told her that the bearer of the letter would inform Taro when she was to be released so he could be at the pier to meet her.

The letter eased her anxiety for a while, but as soon as she was released and boarded the launch for San Francisco, new fears rose up to smother her with a feeling almost of dread.

The early morning mist had become a light chilling rain, and on the pier black umbrellas bobbed here and there, making the task of recognition even harder. Hana searched desperately for a face that resembled the photo she had studied so long and hard. Suppose he hadn't come. What would she do then?

Hana took a deep breath, lifted her head and walked slowly from the launch. The moment she was on the pier, a man in a black coat, wearing a derby and carrying an umbrella, came quickly to her side. He was of slight build, not much taller than she, and his face was sallow and pale. He bowed stiffly and murmured, "You have had a long trip, Miss Omiya. I hope you are well."

Hana caught her breath. "You are Takeda San?" she asked.

He removed his hat and Hana was further startled to see that he was already turning bald.

"You are Takeda San?" she asked again. He looked older than thirty-one.

"I am afraid I no longer resemble the early photo my parents gave you. I am sorry."

Hana had not meant to begin like this. It was not going well.

"No, no," she said quickly. "It is just that I...that is, I am terribly nervous..." Hana stopped abruptly, too flustered to go on.

"I understand," Taro said gently. "You will feel better when you meet my friends and have some tea. Mr. and Mrs. Toda are expecting you in Oakland. You will be staying with them until..." He couldn't bring himself to mention the marriage just yet and Hana was grateful he hadn't.

He quickly made arrangements to have her baggage sent to Oakland, then led her carefully along the rain-slick pier toward the streetcar that would take them to the ferry.

Hana shuddered at the sight of another boat, and as they climbed to its upper deck she felt a queasy tightening of her stomach.

"I hope it will not rock too much," she said anxiously. "Is it many hours to your city?"

Taro laughed for the first time since their meeting, revealing the gold fillings of his teeth. "Oakland is just across the bay," he explained. "We will be there in twenty minutes."

Raising a hand to cover her mouth, Hana laughed with him and suddenly felt better. I am in America now, she thought, and this is the man I came to marry. Then she sat down carefully beside Taro, so no part of their clothing touched. ❖

All Summer in a Day

by Ray Bradbury

"Ready?"

"Ready."

"Now?"

"Soon."

"Do the scientists really know? Will it happen today, will it?"

"Look, look; see for yourself!"

The children pressed to each other like so many roses, so many weeds, intermixed, peering out for a look at the hidden sun.

It rained.

It had been raining for seven years; thousands upon thousands of days compounded and filled from one end to the other with rain, with the drum and gush of water, with the sweet crystal fall of showers and the **concussion** of storms so heavy they were tidal waves come over the islands. A thousand forests had been crushed under the rain and grown up a thousand times to be crushed again. And this was the way life was forever on the planet Venus, and this was the schoolroom of the children of the rocket men and women who had come to a raining world to set up civilization and live out their lives.

"It's stopping, it's stopping!"

"Yes, yes!"

Margot stood apart from them, from these children who could never remember a time when there wasn't rain and rain and rain. They were all nine years old, and if there had been a day, seven years ago, when the sun came out for an hour and showed its face to the **stunned** world, they could not recall. Sometimes, at night, she heard them stir, in remembrance, and she knew they were dreaming and remembering gold or a yellow crayon or a coin large enough to buy the world with. She knew they thought they remembered a warmness, like a blushing in the face, in the body, in the arms and legs and trembling hands. But

....

concussion violent shaking
stunned shocked

then they always awoke to the **tatting drum**, the endless shaking down of clear bead necklaces upon the roof, the walk, the gardens, the forests, and their dreams were gone.

All day yesterday they had read in class about the sun. About how like a lemon it was, and how hot. And they had written small stories or essays or poems about it: *I think the sun is a flower / That blooms for just one hour.* That was Margot's poem, read in a quiet voice in the still classroom while the rain was falling outside.

"Aw, you didn't write that!" protested one of the boys.

"I did," said Margot. "I did."

"William!" said the teacher.

But that was yesterday. Now the rain was **slackening**, and the children were crushed in the great thick windows.

"Where's teacher?"

"She'll be back."

"She'd better hurry; we'll miss it!"

They turned on themselves, like a feverish wheel, all tumbling spokes.

Margot stood alone. She was a very frail girl who looked as if she had been lost in the rain for years and the rain had washed out the blue from her eyes and the red from her mouth and the yellow from her hair. She was an old photograph dusted from an album, whitened away, and if

----

tatting drum the sound of rain
slackening slowing down

she spoke at all her voice would be a ghost. Now she stood, separate, staring at the rain and the loud wet world beyond the huge glass.

"What're *you* looking at?" said William.

Margot said nothing.

"Speak when you're spoken to." He gave her a shove. But she did not move; rather she let herself be moved only by him and nothing else.

They edged away from her, they would not look at her. She felt them go away. And this was because she would play no games with them in the echoing tunnels of the underground city. If they tagged her and ran, she stood blinking after them and did not follow. When the class sang songs about happiness and life and games her lips barely moved. Only when they sang about the sun and the summer did her lips move as she watched the drenched windows.

And then, of course, the biggest crime of all was that she had come here only five years ago from Earth, and she remembered the sun and the way the sun was and the sky was when she was four in Ohio. And they, they had been on Venus all their lives, and they had been only two years old when last the sun came out and had long since forgotten the color and heat of it and the way it really was. But Margot remembered.

"It's like a penny," she said once, eyes closed.

"No it's not!" the children cried.

"It's like a fire," she said, "in the stove."

"You're lying, you don't remember!" cried the children.

But she remembered and stood quietly apart from all of them and watched the patterning windows. And once, a month ago, she had refused to shower in the school shower rooms, had clutched her hands to her ears and over her head, screaming the water mustn't touch her head. So after that, **dimly**, dimly, she sensed it, she was different and they knew her difference and kept away.

There was talk that her father and mother were taking her back to Earth next year; it seemed vital to her that they do so, though it would mean the loss of thousands of dollars to her family. And so, the children hated her for all these reasons of big and little consequence. They hated her pale snow face, her waiting silence, her thinness, and her possible future.

"Get away!" The boy gave her another push. "What're you waiting for?"

Then, for the first time, she turned and looked at him. And what she was waiting for was in her eyes.

"Well, don't wait around here!" cried the boy savagely.

"You won't see nothing!"

Her lips moved.

"Nothing!" he cried. "It was all a joke, wasn't it?" He turned to the other children. "Nothing's happening today. *Is* it?"

....

dimly indistinctly, faintly, or dully

They all blinked at him and then, understanding, laughed and shook their heads.

"Nothing, nothing!"

"Oh, but," Margot whispered, her eyes helpless. "But this is the day, the scientists predict, they say, they *know*, the sun . . ."

"All a joke!" said the boy, and seized her roughly. "Hey, everyone, let's put her in a closet before the teacher comes!"

"No," said Margot, falling back.

They surged about her, caught her up and bore her, protesting, and then pleading, and then crying, back into a tunnel, a room, a closet, where they slammed and locked the door. They stood looking at the door and saw it tremble from her beating and throwing herself against it. They heard her muffled cries. Then, smiling, they turned and went out and back down the tunnel, just as the teacher arrived.

"Ready, children?" She glanced at her watch.

"Yes!" said everyone.

"Are we all here?"

"Yes!"

The rain slackened still more.

They crowded to the huge door.

The rain stopped.

It was as if, in the midst of a film concerning an avalanche, a tornado, a hurricane, a volcanic eruption, something had, first, gone wrong with the sound apparatus, thus muffling and finally cutting off all noise, all of the blasts and repercussions and thunders, and then, second, ripped the film from the projector and inserted in its place a beautiful tropical slide which did not move or tremor. The world ground to a standstill. The silence was so immense and unbelievable that you felt your ears had been stuffed or you had lost your hearing altogether. The children put their hands to their ears. They stood apart. The door slid back and the smell of the silent, waiting world came in to them.

The sun came out.

It was the color of flaming bronze and it was very large. And the sky around it was a blazing blue tile color. And the jungle burned with sunlight as the children, released from their spell, rushed out, yelling into the springtime.

"Now, don't go too far," called the teacher after them. "You've only two hours, you know. You wouldn't want to get caught out!"

But they were running and turning their faces up to the sky and feeling the sun on their cheeks like a warm iron; they were taking off their jackets and letting the sun burn their arms.

"Oh, it's better than the sun lamps, isn't it?"

"Much, much better!"

They stopped running and stood in the great jungle that covered Venus, that grew and never stopped growing,

tumultuously, even as you watched it. It was a nest of octopuses, clustering up great arms of fleshlike weed, wavering, flowering in this brief spring. It was the color of rubber and ash, this jungle, from the many years without sun. It was the color of stones and white cheeses and ink, and it was the color of the moon.

The children lay out, laughing, on the jungle mattress, and heard it sigh and squeak under them resilient and alive. They ran among the trees, they slipped and fell, they pushed each other, they played hide-and-seek and tag, but most of all they squinted at the sun until the tears ran down their faces; they put their hands up to that yellowness and that amazing blueness and they breathed of the fresh, fresh air and listened and listened to the silence which suspended them in a blessed sea of no sound and no motion. They looked at everything and savored everything. Then, wildly, like animals escaped from their caves, they ran and ran in shouting circles. They ran for an hour and did not stop running.

And then—

In the midst of their running one of the girls wailed. Everyone stopped.

The girl, standing in the open, held out her hand. "Oh, look, look," she said, trembling.

They came slowly to look at her opened palm.

....

tumultuously in a disorderly way

In the center of it, cupped and huge, was a single raindrop. She began to cry, looking at it. They glanced quietly at the sun.

"Oh. Oh."

A few cold drops fell on their noses and their cheeks and their mouths. The sun faded behind a stir of mist. A wind blew cold around them. They turned and started to walk back toward the underground house, their hands at their sides, their smiles vanishing away.

A boom of thunder startled them and like leaves before a new hurricane, they tumbled upon each other and ran. Lightning struck ten miles away, five miles away, a mile, a half mile. The sky darkened into midnight in a flash.

They stood in the doorway of the underground for a moment until it was raining hard. Then they closed the door and heard the gigantic sound of the rain falling in tons and avalanches, everywhere and forever.

"Will it be seven more years?"

"Yes. Seven."

Then one of them gave a little cry.

"Margot!"

"What?"

"She's still in the closet where we locked her."

"Margot."

They stood as if someone had driven them, like so many stakes, into the floor. They looked at each other and then looked away. They glanced out at the world that was raining now and raining and raining steadily. They could not meet each other's glances. Their faces were solemn and pale. They looked at their hands and feet, their faces down.

"Margot."

One of the girls said, "Well …?" No one moved.

"Go on," whispered the girl.

They walked slowly down the hall in the sound of cold rain. They turned through the doorway to the room in the sound of the storm and thunder, lightning on their faces, blue and terrible. They walked over to the closet door slowly and stood by it.

Behind the closet door was only silence.

They unlocked the door, even more slowly, and let Margot out. ❖

The Pasture

by Robert Frost

I'm going out to clean the pasture spring;
I'll only stop to rake the leaves away
(And wait to watch the clear water, I may):
I **shan't** be gone long.—You come too.

I'm going out to fetch the little calf
That's standing by the mother. It's so young
It **totters** when she licks it with her tongue.
I shan't be gone long.—You come too. ❖

....

shan't contraction for "shall not"
totters stands unsteadily; wobbles

The Morns Are Meeker Than They Were

by Emily Dickinson

The morns are **meeker** than they were—
The nuts are getting brown—
The berry's cheek is plumper—
The Rose is out of town.

The Maple wears a **gayer** scarf—
The field a **scarlet** gown—
Lest I should be old fashioned
I'll put a **trinket** on. ❖

....

meeker milder; gentler
gayer brighter; more cheerful
scarlet bright red
lest for fear that
trinket a small ornament, such as piece of jewelry

I Wandered Lonely as a Cloud

by William Wordsworth

I wandered lonely as a cloud
    That floats on high o'er **vales** and hills,
When all at once I saw a crowd,—
    A **host** of golden daffodils
Beside the lake, beneath the trees,
Fluttering and dancing in the breeze.

Continuous as the stars that shine
    And twinkle on the Milky Way,
They stretched in never-ending line
    Along the **margin** of a bay:
Ten thousand saw I, at a glance,
Tossing their heads in **sprightly** dance.

vales valleys
host a great many
margin edge
sprightly spirited; lively

The waves beside them danced, but they
    Outdid the sparkling waves in **glee**;
A poet could not but be gay
    In such a **jocund** company;
I gazed—and gazed—but little thought
What wealth the show to me had brought.

For **oft**, when on my couch I lie,
    In **vacant** or in **pensive** mood,
They flash upon that inward eye
    Which is the **bliss** of **solitude**;
And then my heart with pleasure fills,
And dances with the daffodils. ❖

----

glee joy; delight
jocund merry; happy
oft often
vacant without activity
pensive thoughtful
bliss joy; great happiness
solitude the state of being alone

Until I Saw the Sea

by Lilian Moore

Until I saw the sea
I did not know
that wind
could wrinkle water so.

I never knew
that sun
could **splinter** a whole sea of blue.

Nor
did I know before
a sea breathes in and out
upon a shore.

splinter to split into thin pieces

The Voice

by William Oandasan

"first there is a word
the word is the song"

1

song gives birth to
the song and dance
as the dance steps
the story speaks

2

the icy mountain water
that pierces the deep thirst
drums my fire
drums my **medicine pouch**

---

medicine pouch a bag that contains sacred or spiritual items

3

deep within my blood
a feather in the sky
foam on clear water
Tayko-mol!

4

free as the bear
and tall as redwoods
throb my blood roots
when spirits ride high

5

a valley ripe with acorns
and yellow poppies everywhere
as i stand here
dreaming of you

6

jolting my dream
an old man struggling
with an eel   his coat appears
disheveled and empty

Tayko-mol the creator of the Yuki; the Solitary Walker
disheveled messy

7

in a sacred manner
i sang and waited
     a lick of your blood
     i must take, **reverently**, deer

8

for you, blue corn baby,
my thoughts
on a melody of love
sail the sky

9

around fire on my head
a rattlesnake hisses and slithers
then flies up   out of sight
fighting in sleep i cry out

10

the snake in my spine is tensing
for combat
thoughts become forced and tight
the air is a sharp knife

....

reverently with great respect

11

from under me today
the earth was pulled
balancing on a sharp mountain ridge
i search for a plain

12

Tayko-mol has not left us
but lives in the pulse
of our words, and waits
in the **azure** for us all ❖

---

azure bright blue color in the sky

Elegy for My Brother Poet Filipino and Yuki Indian

for William Oandasan, 1947–1992
by Vince Gotera

Jagged as chipped **obsidian** are the words
of some Indian poets, knowing their infant
death rate is seven times greater than

the American average—but your words,
Oandasan, are gentle raindrops, hummingbird
wings simmering in ancient Sequoia forest.

....

obsidian a hard, dark, glasslike rock

In the Badlands, the Lakota retraced the trail
of Chief Big Foot back to **Wounded Knee**, seven
generations after that bloodletting—but your

words live on in the blood, snowflake red platelets
swimming in the brain. In Manila, **Ferdinand
and Imelda** buried poets in iron and tarmac—

but your words are lizards, green and swift,
dragonflies in a painted desert. Helicopter
gunships threatened peasants at harvest time

in **Vietnam, El Salvador, Afghanistan**
—but your words live on in sacred corn,
in wheat's amber waves, in the holy words

of **Tayko-mol**. Oandasan, your poems fly like
rainbow-feathered spiders in seven directions—
mountain, valley, forest, city, ocean, sky, home. ❖

....

Wounded Knee the site of a massacre of Native Americans in 1890; the site of a protest about living conditions on the Pine Ridge Indian Reservation in 1973

Ferdinand and Imelda Filipino dictator Ferdinand Marcos and his wife Imelda

Vietnam, El Salvador, Afghanistan armed conflicts the United States was involved in

Tayko-mol the creator of the Yuki; the Solitary Walker

Borderbus

by Juan Felipe Herrera

A dónde vamos where are we going

Speak in English or the guard is going to come

A dónde vamos where are we going

Speak in English or the guard is gonna get us **hermana**

Pero qué hicimos but what did we do

Speak in English come on

Nomás sé unas pocas palabras I just know a few words

You better figure it out hermana the guard is right there

See the bus driver

....

hermana Spanish for "sister"

Tantos días y ni sabíamos para donde íbamos
So many days and we didn't even know where we were
headed

I know where we're going
Where we always go

To some **detention center** to some fingerprinting hall
or cube
Some warehouse warehouse after warehouse

Pero ya nos investigaron ya cruzamos ya nos cacharon
Los federales del bordo qué más quieren
But they already questioned us we already crossed over they
already grabbed us the Border Patrol what more do
they want

We are on the bus now
that is all

A dónde vamos te digo salí desde Honduras
No hemos comido nada y dónde vamos a dormir

---

detention center a facility where people, often illegal immigrants or refugees,
are held for a short period

Where are we going I am telling you I came from Honduras
We haven't eaten anything and where are we going to sleep

I don't want to talk about it just tell them
That you came from nowhere
I came from nowhere
And we crossed the border from nowhere
And now you and me and everybody else here is
On a bus to nowehere you got it?

Pero por eso nos venimos para salir de la nada
But that's why we came to leave all that nothing behind

When the bus stops there will be more nothing
We're here hermana

Y esas gentes quiénes son
no quieren que siga el camión
No quieren que sigamos
Están bloqueando el bus
A dónde vamos ahora
Those people there who are they
they don't want the bus to keep going
they don't want us to keep going
now they are blocking the bus
so where do we go

What?

He tardado 47 días para llegar acá no fue fácil hermana
45 días desde Honduras con los coyotes los que se—bueno
ya sabes lo que les hicieron a las chicas allí mero en frente
de nosotros pero qué íbamos a hacer y los trenes los trenes
cómo diré hermana cientos de
nosotros como gallinas como topos en jaulas y verduras
pudriendóse en los trenes de miles me oyes de miles y se
resbalaban
de los techos y los desiertos de Arizona de Tajas sed y
hambre
sed y hambre dos cosas sed y hambre día tras día hermana
y ahora aquí en este camión y quién sabe a dónde
vamos hermana fijate vengo desde Brownsville dónde nos
amarraron
y ahora en California pero todavía no entramos y todavía
el bordo
está por delante
It took me 47 days to get here it wasn't easy hermana
45 days from Honduras with the coyotes the ones that
— well
you know what they did to las chicas
right there in front of us so what were we supposed
to do and the trains the trains how can I tell you hermana
hundreds
of us like chickens like gophers in cages and vegetables

rotting on trains of thousands you hear me of thousands
and they slid
from the rooftops and the deserts of Arizona and Texas
thirst and hunger
thirst and hunger two things thirst and hunger day after
day hermana
and now here on this bus of who-knows-where we are going
hermana listen I come from Brownsville where they tied us
up
and now in California but still we're not inside and still the
border
lies ahead of us

I told you to speak in English even un poquito
the guard is going to think we are doing something
people are screaming outside
they want to push the bus back

Pero para dónde le damos hermana
por eso me vine
le quebraron las piernas a mi padre
las pandillas mataron a mi hijo
solo quiero que estemos juntos
tantos años hermana
separados
But where do we go hermana
that's why I came here

they broke my father's legs
gangs killed my son
I just want us to be together
so many years hermana
pulled apart

What?

Mi madre me dijo que lo más importante
es la libertad la bondad y la buenas acciones
con el prójimo
My mother told me that the most important thing
is freedom kindness and doing good
for others

What are you talking about?
I told you to be quiet

La libertad viene desde muy adentro
allí reside todo el dolor de todo el mundo
el momento en que purguemos ese dolor de nuestras
entrañas
seremos libres y en ese momento tenemos que
llenarnos de todo el dolor de todos los seres
para liberarlos a ellos mismos
Freedom comes from deep inside
all the pain of the world lives there

the second we cleanse that pain from our guts
we shall be free and in that moment we have to
fill ourselves up with all the pain of all beings
to free them—all of them

The guard is coming well
now what   maybe they'll take us
to another detention center we'll eat we'll have a floor
a blanket toilets water and each other
for a while

No somos nada y venimos de la nada
pero esa nada lo es todo si la nutres de amor
por eso venceremos
We are nothing and we come from nothing
but that nothing is everything, if you feed it with love
that is why we will **triumph**

We are everything hermana
Because we come from everything ❖

---

triumph to achieve victory

Influential People

Raphael Sanzio
as a young man

The Child of Urbino

by Louise de la Ramée

Long ago in the city of Urbino there lived a master potter named Benedetto. Benedetto had a daughter, Pacifica, whom he loved very much. But the dearest thing in the world to him—dearer even then Pacifica—was his pottery, and his greatest sorrow was that he had no son to carry on his art. The sorrow was the greater because across the mountains a younger man was gaining fame as a potter, and in time seemed likely to outdo Benedetto and the pottery of Urbino.

Benedetto had a neighbor, and this neighbor had a son, a little fair-haired, grave-eyed child of seven, named Raphael. Raphael's father was an artist, and very early the child began to learn from him to hold the brush and mix colors. He was often seen, too, in the workshop of Benedetto, for the potter loved the boy, both for himself, and for the love that he already showed for art. For hours at a time Raphael would stand quietly beside the old man as he worked, noting each detail of the potter's skill, and storing up in his little head the things he learned there.

He was a friend, too, of the tall, dark-eyed Pacifica, who was ever ready to stop her work to play with him. But best of all, he loved big, gentle Luca. Luca had come down from the hills to learn the potter's trade from Benedetto. He was tall and straight, and he loved Benedetto's daughter with all his heart.

But, alas, poor Luca, good and handsome though he was, would never be an artist! He knew it. He knew also that Benedetto would never look with **favor** upon any but a great artist as the husband of Pacifica, and he **despaired** of ever winning her. He often told his trouble to Raphael, who felt very sorry for the young man and comforted him as best he could.

One day Luca came to Raphael in deep trouble. An order had come from the duke for a great jar and platter. It was to be sent over the mountains as a gift to the duke's cousin. Everyone in the potter's workshop must strive to fill the order in a way that would be pleasing to the duke. Benedetto had let it be known that the man who was lucky enough to please the duke might become Benedetto's partner and likewise his son-in-law. Poor Luca was in

favor approval
despaired lost all hope

despair. He knew very well that his chance of winning Pacifica was gone.

Raphael's tender heart was touched.

"How long do you have to complete this work, Luca?" he asked hopefully.

"Three months," answered Luca, "but it makes no difference. I could never do it in three years."

Raphael thought for a long while. At last, putting his hand in Luca's, he said, "Luca, let me try to paint a jar and platter."

If Luca had not been so miserable, the sight of the little fellow would have made him laugh.

"Please, Luca," pleaded the child. "I can paint, you know. I have often watched Benedetto at work. Please, Luca, it can do no harm."

Finally, rather than hurt the boy's feelings, Luca **assented**.

Day after day Raphael climbed the stairs to Luca's workroom. Pacifica, watching him, thought he went to watch and cheer Luca, and was sad because she knew that his faithfulness would do nothing toward helping Luca win the prize.

But up in the bare **garret** the child was working hard. How thankful he was for the hours spent with Benedetto,

....

assented agreed
garret an attic room

and for the lessons of his father, the painter. How anxiously he toiled, painting and rubbing out, and painting again. Not a word did he breathe about his work, nor would he even allow Luca to look at what he did. Each night he covered it carefully so that no one might catch a glimpse of it. Meanwhile Luca was working away hopelessly, too sad to notice his little friend.

At last, the day before the end of the three months, Raphael called Luca to see his work. Trembling with eagerness, he uncovered his jar and platter and showed them to his friend.

One glance was enough. The astonished youth fell on his knees, crying out in wonder at the beauty of the child's work.

Raphael danced up and down with joy.

"But, Raphael," cried poor Luca, "it can do me no good. This is your work. It would be cheating for me to win Pacifica this way. I could not do it."

"Wait," said the child. "I have a plan."

On the next day, the duke was to come to choose his pottery. From all the country round the youth had gathered, bringing their work to be judged. The pottery was placed on benches in the great workroom, each piece being marked with a number instead of a name, in order that the judges might not know whose work it was, and that the judgment should be quite fair.

In the outer room Benedetto and a few friends waited for the duke to come. Little Raphael was there, very pale, clinging to his father's hand.

When the duke appeared, Benedetto led the way to his workroom. The duke passed along the row of jars and platters, praising each. At last, he stopped.

"This is beyond all comparison," he said turning to the potter. "Master Benedetto, whose work is this?"

Benedetto stepped forward and looked at the pottery. "It can be none of my people," he said. "I have no one in my workshop who could do work such as that. Number eleven," he added, looking at the gathering of potters, "step forward. The duke has chosen your work."

In the hush that followed, the child Raphael stepped out.

"I painted it," he said with a pleased smile. "I, Raphael."

Immediately the room was in confusion. The astonished potters gathered about the child, while Benedetto and Raphael's father looked on in amazement.

With tears in his eyes, the duke took a jewel that hung on a gold chain about his neck and placed it over Raphael's shoulders. "This is your first reward," he said. "You will have many, O wondrous child, who shall live when we are dust!"

Raphael kissed the duke's hand. Then he turned to his father. "Is it true," he asked, "that my jar and platter have been chosen?"

His father could only bow his head. "Then," said Raphael, looking up bravely at Benedetto, "Master, I claim the prize."

There was a little ripple of laughter.

"I am your pupil," said the child. "If you had not taught me your secrets, I could never have painted these. Now, dear Master, I give my right to my friend, Luca, who is the honestest man in all the world, and does love Pacifica as no other can do."

Benedetto burst into tears. "Indeed," he said, "I can refuse him nothing. He will give such glory to Urbino as the world has never seen."

And the words that Benedetto spoke were fulfilled in the years to come. ❖

Mary Cassatt

Mary Cassatt:
Artist and Trailblazer

by Vanessa Wright

One day in Paris, in 1851, a seven-year-old American girl named Mary Cassatt went with her family to visit the Louvre, one of the world's greatest art museums. The little girl gazed up in wonder at paintings of the old masters, such as Leonardo da Vinci's *Mona Lisa*, Titian's mythical scenes, and Rembrandt's shadowy, **brooding** landscapes.

"Someday," she said to herself, "I will be as great an artist as they."

A few years later, young Mary Cassatt returned with her family to America. With the images she had seen in Paris still aglow in her mind, she wanted more than ever to become a professional artist. "In fact," she said to a friend, "I am going to paint better than the old masters!"

....
brooding gloomy

As soon as she was old enough, Cassatt entered the Pennsylvania Academy of Fine Arts. She took drawing classes, but was disappointed because the Academy's art collection had very few great paintings for her to study. At that time, not even the best American museums had collections that could compare with the great paintings hanging in the Louvre.

Cassatt remembered watching art students in Paris learn to paint by copying the great works in the Louvre. "If I want to be a serious painter," she thought, "it seems I must return to Europe."

Cassatt's goal was clear, but there were many obstacles in her path. The year was 1865. Women did not have the right to vote. They were not allowed to attend the best art schools. In general, women were not expected or encouraged to become artists. And they were definitely not supposed to travel **abroad** alone. So when Cassatt told her father that she wished to study in Europe and become a professional artist, he strongly **opposed** her wishes.

But Cassatt **persisted**. She discussed, explained, and argued with her father until he changed his mind. Rather than resist her, he decided to support her artistic **ambitions**. And so in 1866, when Cassatt was twenty-two

....

abroad outside one's home country
opposed disagreed with
persisted continued with determination
ambitions goals; strong desires to achieve

years old, she moved back to Paris, ready to fulfill her dreams.

In Paris, Cassatt studied with successful artists. She carefully copied paintings in the Louvre. She also packed up her brushes, rode out to the countryside, and painted the people and landscapes that caught her fancy.

Many people admired Cassatt's paintings of the French countryside. Her teachers admired them so much that they encouraged her to try to get them displayed in the great annual art exhibition called the Salon. At the Salon, some paintings were awarded ribbons or medals, but almost all artists whose work was chosen for the Salon would become successful. And, on the other side, it was almost impossible to succeed as a painter without exhibiting at the Salon.

It was not easy to get a painting picked for exhibition in the Salon. The jury that judged the paintings only liked a certain kind of art. They chose paintings that resembled the work of the old masters: dark and serious, with smooth, blended colors. They wanted the subjects to be from history, mythology, or literature, arranged in formal poses, and painted to look perfect instead of like real people. They did not welcome originality.

The jury rejected the first painting Cassatt submitted for the Salon. But the next year, they accepted a painting, very much in the style of the old masters, showing a peasant woman sitting and holding a mandolin.

While it was a great honor to be chosen, Cassatt soon grew restless. She preferred to paint with bright colors and loose strokes. She liked painting ordinary people doing ordinary things. She was developing her own style, but it was not a style that the Salon's jury liked. "What should I do?" she wondered. "Should I paint to please the jurors of the Salon, or should I paint my own way?"

One day, as Cassatt walked past a gallery window, she saw a pastel drawing by a boldly original French artist, Edgar Degas. She stopped in front of the window and stared at it. She could not tear herself away. The next day she returned to look at Degas' work, and the next, and the next. "I used to go and flatten my nose against that window and absorb all I could of his art," she wrote to a friend. "It changed my life. I saw art then as I wanted to see it."

Some time later, Degas saw one of Cassatt's portraits. He noticed that while she painted with the skill and grace of the old masters, she also mixed in the ideas and **techniques** of newer artists. In her work, he recognized a **kindred spirit**. It is said that after he looked at her painting, he cried to his friend, "There is someone who feels as I do!"

Edgar Degas was one of the first artists known as the Impressionists, a group that also included Claude Monet

....

techniques methods; ways of doing something
kindred spirit someone who shares similar beliefs and values

and Auguste Renoir. The Impressionists were a group of **experimental** artists who tried to capture on canvas a brief but true impression of people, places, or objects. They abandoned the old masters' dark colors and smooth brushstrokes. Instead, they used bright, lively colors, and bold lines and brushstrokes. Instead of painting people in stiff, formal poses, they captured people in **fleeting** moments of everyday life. Degas, for example, painted ballet dancers in rehearsal or **laundresses** at work.

Degas saw hints of Impressionism in Cassatt's painting. So he hurried to her studio and invited her to exhibit with his group instead of with the Salon. For Cassatt, it meant giving up the success guaranteed by exhibiting with the Salon, but she accepted the offer. Later, she wrote to her friend, "At last I could work with complete independence without concerning myself with the eventual judgment of a jury. I hated **conventional** art. I began to live."

A year after she met Degas, Cassatt painted *Little Girl in a Blue Armchair*. In the painting, a little girl sits **sprawled** in a big, comfy chair, with one hand casually reaching behind her head. A small dog sleeps on another chair nearby. The little girl does not look out from the painting. Her expression seems a little bored, as though she had

experimental trying new things
fleeting passing quickly
laundresses women who do other people's laundry for pay
conventional ordinary; following accepted rules or practices
sprawled spread out

Cassatt's *Little Girl in a Blue Armchair*, 1878

just collapsed into the chair and heaved a big sigh while wishing she had something else to do. The designs on the blue chairs are **rendered** with swift brushstrokes. Certainly, the Salon jury would not have approved of this painting!

As Cassatt experimented with the Impressionists' techniques, she began to develop her own individual style. For her subjects, she did not choose the usual landscapes or cityscapes. Instead, she often painted women going about their daily tasks, or mothers and their children sharing tender, trusting moments. Although Cassatt herself never

rendered made

had children, perhaps no artist has better captured the bond between mother and child.

Cassatt continued to try new techniques. After attending an exhibition of Japanese wood-block prints, she experimented with making her own prints and engravings. Her friend Degas was greatly impressed, and thought her prints to be some of her best work.

Although Cassatt spent most of her life in Paris, she returned sometimes to the United States. She advised wealthy Americans who wished to buy and exhibit great European art, both the old masters as well as the best of the new paintings. More than any other person, Mary Cassatt helped introduce Americans to the work of the Impressionists. Some of the pieces Cassatt helped purchase still hang in American museums today.

Mary Cassatt was a **trailblazer**. Though women in her time had little freedom and few choices, she achieved her ambition to become a professional artist. She developed a style all her own, and chose the subjects that suited her, regardless of official opinions. She was the only American to exhibit with the Impressionists, and helped bridge the art gap between Europe and the United States.

"I have not done all I wanted to," she wrote before her death, "but I tried to make a good fight." ❖

....

trailblazer one who does something new, who opens a new path for others to follow

Marian Anderson

Marian Anderson Sings

by Mara Rockliff

The instant Marian Anderson stepped off the train in Washington, D.C., she found herself surrounded by reporters. Questions flew at her from every side.

The Daughters of the American Revolution have refused to let you sing at Constitution Hall because you are a Negro. How does that make you feel?

Are you insulted?

Are you angry?

What are you going to do?

For many of their questions, Anderson had no answer. But the answer to the last question was clear. She would do what she had always done, what she did best. She would sing.

Even as a little girl in Philadelphia, singing in her church choir, Marian Anderson knew her **destiny** lay in her rich, wide-ranging voice. But her father died when she was twelve. Her mother worked long hours cleaning houses and taking in laundry. She earned barely enough to feed and clothe her three daughters. Music lessons for young Marian seemed just a dream, but talent alone was not enough. She needed training.

A local music teacher generously offered Marian free lessons. But it was not long before the teacher said she'd taught her all she could. If Marian was really serious about her music, she should go to music school. Perhaps she could win a scholarship.

Marian Anderson rode the **trolley** downtown to the school. There she joined a long line of other excited **applicants**. Patiently, she waited for her turn. But when she reached the window, the clerk—a white girl her own age—looked right past her to the next person in line. She watched, bewildered, as the girl handed forms to everyone but her. Finally, she turned to Anderson and said, "What do you want?"

Anderson asked for an application form. The girl stared at her coldly. "We don't take colored," she said. Shocked and hurt, Anderson walked out.

....

destiny a person's fate in life
trolley a streetcar
applicants people who have applied for something

At home, her mother urged her not to give up. If she was meant to sing, there would be a way. And there was. An Italian voice teacher who had trained many opera stars heard her sing and agreed to take her as his student. But his fees were more than she could possibly afford. Sadly, Anderson thanked him for his time and left.

However, her friends and neighbors were not about to let "our Marian" miss out on such an opportunity. They put on a benefit concert at the church and raised $600—enough for a whole year of voice lessons.

The work was hard. Marian sang splendidly without training, but she needed to learn to control her voice like a professional. She even needed to learn to breathe differently. She practiced her exercises over and over. And she learned new songs—Italian, German, French. At first, she simply memorized the words syllable by syllable. But how could she give true feeling to a song she didn't understand? So she had to study languages as well.

Those struggles were behind her now. Touring Europe, she'd become a huge **sensation**. Audiences crowded into concert halls to hear the elegant American **contralto**. With **regal poise**, she would stand by the piano, eyes closed, her velvety, expressive voice expanding to fill every corner of the room.

....

sensation someone who causes great excitement
contralto a female singer with a low voice
regal royal; like a king or queen
poise calm, confident self-assurance

Once, after a concert, the legendary conductor Arturo Toscanini came backstage. "Yours is a voice," he told Anderson, "such as one hears once in a hundred years."

When she returned to the United States, fame and success followed. Here, too, she was invited to sing in the finest concert halls, often to sellout crowds. But across the footlights Anderson often saw only white faces. In many cities, in the South especially, people of her own race had to sit up in the balcony. And, as warmly as an audience applauded, after the show a restaurant or hotel manager might coldly turn her away.

Anderson responded to these slights with quiet dignity. She was determined not to let other people's fear and **ignorance** pull her away from what really mattered—her music.

The singer's popularity continued to grow. Her manager worked hard to find concert halls big enough to hold Anderson's growing audiences. When her tour schedule brought her to Washington, D.C., in 1939, the choice was obvious: the city's largest and grandest concert **venue**, Constitution Hall.

Anderson's manager wrote to make arrangements. The date he wanted was already taken, he was told. He suggested other dates in April. He was told that those were taken, too. In fact, no dates were available at all.

....

ignorance lack of knowledge
venue the location where a special event or gathering occurs

Could this be true? Suspicious, the manager asked a well-known white pianist to try to book the hall. The answer came back: the pianist could have his pick of any date that spring.

The truth quickly came out. Constitution Hall was owned by the Daughters of the American Revolution. Only women—white women—whose ancestors had fought the British were allowed to join this group. And the DAR would not rent Constitution Hall to any African American performer, even one as widely admired as Marian Anderson.

News of this refusal outraged Anderson's many fans. Fellow musicians canceled their performances. Among them was the famous violinist, Jascha Heifetz, who said, "I am ashamed to play at Constitution Hall." Fiorello LaGuardia, the mayor of New York, sent the DAR a telegram: "No hall is too good for Marian Anderson." The First Lady, Eleanor Roosevelt, even resigned from the DAR in protest, making front-page headlines all over the country.

Everywhere Anderson went, reporters swarmed around, demanding a reaction. What could she say? The uproar saddened and embarrassed her. Dignified as always, she refused to speak out publicly against the DAR. Many of the group's members, she knew, disagreed with the national leadership. As she wrote later in her autobiography, she strongly believed that "a whole group should not be

condemned because an individual or section of the group does a thing that is not right."

Anderson had faith that right would always win out in the end. All she wanted was to make beautiful music. She was certain she would find a place to sing.

Then came a surprising invitation—from the United States government. How would Anderson like to sing on Easter Sunday at the Lincoln Memorial? It would be an outdoor concert, free, open to all—and with no **segregation**.

Anderson struggled over her reply. She was a singer, not an activist. She did not enjoy being the center of attention for reasons other than her music. To sing at the Lincoln Memorial would be a bold political statement. At best, she'd feel uncomfortable. At worst, she might find herself at the center of an ugly riot.

"I studied my conscience," she wrote. "I could see that my significance as an individual was small in this affair. I had become, whether I liked it or not, a symbol, representing my people. I had to appear."

Easter Sunday arrived. Hours before the concert started, people began gathering at the Lincoln Memorial. By the time Anderson's car pulled up, the crowd had grown to 75,000. Millions more waited at home by their radios.

....

condemned judged as wrong or evil
segregation the separation of people based on their race

Police led Anderson through the **throng** to a platform in front of the monument. "My heart leaped wildly, and I could not talk," she wrote. "I even wondered whether I would be able to sing."

She barely noticed the many Washington notables who joined her on the platform. Members of President Roosevelt's cabinet, Supreme Court justices, senators, and congressmen were all on hand to hear the celebrated singer.

Anderson looked out at the sea of faces, black and white, women, men, and children. "There seemed to be people as far as the eye could see," she wrote. "The crowd stretched in a great semicircle from the Lincoln Memorial around the reflecting pool on to the shaft of the Washington Monument. I had a feeling that a great wave of good will poured out from these people, almost engulfing me."

Standing tall and determined, Anderson looked like a queen. Inside, though, she was terrified.

The first notes of "The Star-Spangled Banner" boomed over the loudspeakers. For a desperate moment, Anderson felt as if she were choking. Would the words she knew so well refuse to come?

She found her voice. Thousands of voices joined Anderson's as she led her audience in the national anthem. She went on to sing "America," followed by an operatic

---

throng a large crowd

Marian Anderson singing at the Lincoln Memorial,
Washington, D.C., April 9, 1939

aria, Schubert's "Ave Maria," and three traditional African
American spirituals. Her voice soared, powerful, rich,
and thrilling.

When she finished, a great roar went up. The crowd
surged forward. They could not stop cheering and
applauding.

....

aria in an opera, a melody sung by a single voice with orchestra

Of all who gathered that day at the Lincoln Memorial, no one could have been moved more deeply than Marian Anderson. Her courage and faith had been rewarded. America had reached out to embrace one of its greatest singers.

"I am overwhelmed," Anderson told the crowd. "I can't tell you what you have done for me today. I thank you from the bottom of my heart again and again." ❖

Marian Anderson: Legendary Singer

On February 27, 1897, Marian Anderson, one of America's great talents, was born. Growing up in South Philadelphia, Anderson attended the Union Baptist Church with her two sisters and parents. It was here, where all three girls sang in the youth choir, that Anderson's extraordinary singing ability first became evident. Anderson's voice was so **versatile** she could sing parts for any of the voice types— soprano, alto, tenor, or bass. Recognizing her talent, the choir master promoted her from the youth to the adult choir at the young age of 14. Her fellow church-goers were so impressed they started to a "Marian Anderson Future Fund" to pay for her to take voice lessons.

As a teen, Anderson continued her education at the South Philadelphia High School for Girls. However, she would face discrimination as music **conservatories** denied her admission because of her race. Her immense talent drew a large number of fans who would support her in her undertakings though. Anderson studied with the famous voice teacher Giuseppe Boghetti. He was so impressed by her majestic voice he gave her free lessons. Her talent enabled her to compete with over 300 singers and win the

versatile able to adapt or be used in many different ways
conservatories schools that train musicians and singers

opportunity to perform with the New York Philharmonic Orchestra in New York City. She also sang with the Philadelphia Symphony and toured African American colleges in the American South.

Marian Anderson also won scholarships to study abroad. She performed before the rulers of countries such as Sweden, Norway, Denmark and England. In 1935, she made her European **debut** at the Paris Opera House, delighting fans. Later that year, Anderson returned to the United States to make her New York concert debut at famed Carnegie Hall. Anderson's dedication to her art was clear that night as she performed with a cast on her ankle. She had fallen and broken it the night before. One year later, First Lady Eleanor Roosevelt invited Anderson to perform at the White House— the first African American to do so. That evening in 1936, Anderson amazed the President, First Lady, and their guests with her beautiful voice.

While her immense talent was gaining her many fans through the country and world, Anderson, along with her fellow African Americans, was forced to live under the segregationist policies and discriminatory attitudes of the day. When traveling the country, Anderson was subjected to using "colored" waiting rooms, hotels, and train cars. She could not enter the formal dining room of several hotels in which she stayed. To avoid these injustices, Anderson often would drive her own car or stay with local friends while

debut first public performance

on tour. Media in the South would refuse to grant her the respect given other artists. Instead, news reports would refer to her as "Artist Anderson," or "Singer Anderson" instead of the standard "Miss" Anderson.

Despite such bigotry and prejudice, more and more Americans became enchanted with Marian Anderson's voice. As a result, the annual fundraising concert Anderson gave to support Howard University grew in popularity. To accommodate this increased interest, in 1939, the university contacted Constitution Hall in Washington, D.C., in an attempt to book it. However, the owners of the hall—the Daughters of the American Revolution—refused to allow it to be rented to them because of Marian Anderson's race. Many of Anderson's fans were outraged by this discrimination, including Eleanor Roosevelt. She was a member of the Daughters of the American Revolution. In protest of the treatment of Anderson, Roosevelt resigned from the organization. Roosevelt was influential in arranging the concert to be held on Easter Sunday that year in front of the Lincoln Memorial. Over 75,000 people of all races heard Anderson perform "America," "Ave Maria," and "Nobody Knows the Trouble I've Seen" among other selections. Thousands listened on their radios at home. Several years later, the Daughters of the American Revolution invited Anderson to perform at Constitution Hall.

Marian Anderson's groundbreaking accomplishments continued throughout her life. She would become the first

African American to sing at the world-renowned Metropolitan Opera in New York City. When she first appeared on stage, the audience offered her a standing ovation. Anderson received many awards throughout her career, including ones from the city of Philadelphia and the National Association for the Advancement of Colored People (NAACP).

Marian Anderson being awarded the Congressional Gold Medal by U.S. President Jimmy Carter, 1987

Presidents also praised her talent, success, and determination and accomplishments. Anderson embarked on a twelve-country tour sponsored in part by the U.S. Department of State. She was also named a **delegate** to the United Nations and awarded the prestigious Presidential Medal of Freedom. She was the first African American to receive the Congressional Gold Medal. Colleges and universities bestowed over twenty honorary degrees on Anderson as well.

In 1965, Marian Anderson gave her final performance at famed Carnegie Hall in New York City. She retired from performing and lived on her Connecticut farm with her husband. Anderson passed away in 1993 at age 96. ❖

delegate a person who represents other people or an entity (in this case, the United States) in a larger conference or organization (in this case, the United Nations)

Mohandas Gandhi

Mohandas Gandhi:
Truth in Action

by Vanessa Wright

What is the most powerful force mankind can command? Fire? A great army? Nuclear energy? Mohandas Gandhi answered, "Nonviolence is the greatest force **at the disposal of** mankind. It is mightier than the mightiest weapon of destruction **devised** by the **ingenuity** of man."

But how can the calm voice of nonviolence be heard over the howl of a mob or the whine of bullets? What is the power of truth in an unjust world?

---

at the disposal of that can be used as one pleases
devised invented; created; thought up
ingenuity skill or cleverness in inventing

"Thief," thought Mohandas Gandhi. "I am a thief."

Fifteen-year-old Mohandas looked at the gold in his hand. He had stolen it from his brother. It was not his first theft: earlier, he had stolen coins from the family's servants. But now, the gold in his hand burned like a hot coal. He sat down and wrote a letter of confession to his father.

Would his father punish him? Mohandas watched as his father read the note. Tears rolled down his father's cheeks, wetting the paper. But there was no scolding. Silently, his father tore the letter into pieces. Later, Gandhi realized that, in his father's response, he had seen the principle of *Ahimsa*—of nonviolence—in action. He dedicated his life to that principle.

When Gandhi was born in India in 1869, the country was under British rule. As a young man, he sailed to England to finish his schooling. In London, he trained to become a lawyer. On his return to India, he struggled to establish his legal career. Since he was meeting with little success in India, he decided to make the long trip to South Africa, where many Indians lived and worked.

He was **appalled** to find that in some parts of South Africa, Indians were not allowed to vote or to own more than a certain amount of property. They had to be off the streets by 9 p.m., and pay a tax because they were Indian. Once, Gandhi himself purchased a first-class train ticket,

appalled horrified; shocked

only to be told after he had boarded that he had to sit in the third-class compartment reserved for Indians and Africans. When Gandhi refused, he was taken off of the train.

Gandhi knew that such laws were unjust. It was time to tell the truth—and, to take action. So he wrote letters to newspapers, talked with government officials, and held peaceful protests to draw attention to the unjust laws. He also started a group called the Natal Indian Congress, a **forum** in which Indians in South Africa could discuss the problems facing them and decide how to solve them together.

While he was in South Africa, Gandhi developed the idea of *satyagraha*, a word that means "the pursuit of truth." For Gandhi, satyagraha meant the nonviolent struggle against injustice, especially to help those who were poor or suffering due to unjust laws or customs. Gandhi never used violence against his **adversaries**. Satyagraha meant solving problems peacefully, with respect for all.

Satyagraha was not an easy path to follow. Once, a mob of white South Africans threw stones and rotten eggs at Gandhi. Officials offered to take the members of the mob to court. But Gandhi refused. "What is the use?" he asked; "I am sure that, when the truth becomes known, they will be sorry for their conduct."

forum a place for discussion of ideas
adversaries enemies

For about twenty years, Gandhi fought for equal rights for Indians in South Africa. During this time, the news spread about his nonviolent struggles, and many people were drawn to the idea of satyagraha.

In 1915, Gandhi returned with his family to India. Little did he know it, but he was about to face one of the greatest challenges of his life.

In his own home country, Gandhi found his people suffering under the rule of the British. The British had been gaining power in India since the mid-1700s, and had officially taken control of India in 1858. Since taking control, Britain had made laws that imposed harsh taxes and stopped Indian trade with other countries. Under these laws, many Indians became poor. The laws were unjust, but with only a few Indians allowed to participate in the government, how could things be changed?

Eventually, many Indians began to demand independence from Britain. But the people were not unified. They spoke different languages, quarreled over religion and social class, and were scattered across the land in cities and tiny villages, long before telephones or the Internet could connect them. The British had a strong government and an army to enforce their laws. To win their independence, the Indians would have to overcome their differences and work together to defeat their common adversary.

It looked as if no one could unite the Indian people. Then one day in January 1915, a large crowd of Indians, rich and poor, from the cities and the villages, and from every social class, gathered around a dock in Bombay. They were there to cheer the man they hoped would lead them to independence as he had led the Indians in South Africa: Mohandas Gandhi.

First, to get **reacquainted** with his country, Gandhi went around India by train, meeting and talking with the people. He traveled in crowded third-class compartments with hard benches, and sometimes had to sleep standing up. Everywhere he went, he saw poverty and disease.

In 1919, the British passed laws forbidding protest in India. Violence broke out, especially in the city of Amritsar. One British general responded by having his soldiers open fire on a group of men, women, and children in a marketplace. In that terrible incident, 379 people died and more than 1,000 others were injured.

As news of the **massacre** spread, violence threatened to **engulf** the entire country. But Gandhi offered another way. He urged Indians to participate in "noncooperation" against the British. Noncooperation meant that Indians would **boycott** British goods, take their children out of British schools, and pay not a single **rupee** of British taxes.

....

reacquainted introduced to again; familiar with again
massacre the violent killing of a number of helpless, unresisting people
engulf to consume or swallow up
boycott to protest by refusing to buy from or deal with
rupee an Indian coin

Gandhi walking with his followers

Eventually, faced with the firm and unyielding opposition of hundreds of thousands of Indians, the British began to compromise. Where violence had failed, satyagraha had **prevailed**. With satyagraha, said Gandhi, "you can bring the world to your feet."

Still, for Gandhi, it was not enough to bring down British rule. He also wanted to build up India from within. So he reached out to the outcasts of Indian society, the poorest of the poor, called the Untouchables.

prevailed triumphed; won

At that time, most of India's people lived under the caste system. Each person was born into a certain class, or caste, and had to follow its rules. But Untouchables were considered outside the caste system. Everyone shunned them. Members of other castes feared they would be polluted if even the shadow of an Untouchable touched them. But Gandhi called the Untouchables "Children of God" and declared that he would **fast** until something was done to make their lives better. Through his efforts, Untouchables were allowed into temples and invited to participate in Indian assemblies. And the British agreed never to make any law that called a person an "untouchable."

Still, it was not enough. Gandhi also wanted Indians to be **self-sufficient**. He burned piles of British clothing in front of Indians, and encouraged them to spin their own cloth and grow their own food or buy it from each other, instead of from the British. He stopped wearing Western clothes, learned to spin cloth, and wore only a cotton shawl and *dhoti*, a kind of loincloth, which had been spun by Indian hands. He also founded communities where people came together to grow their own food, provide for themselves, and work for the good of all the people in the group.

---

fast to go without eating
self-sufficient able to provide for oneself instead of relying on others

For more than thirty years, Gandhi led the Indians in a nonviolent struggle against the British. And at last, in 1947, the British granted Indians their independence. When Hindus and Muslims started fighting in India, Gandhi went on a fast to try to bring them together.

Sadly, less than six months after India became independent, Gandhi was assassinated as he walked to a prayer meeting. Millions of people around the world mourned his passing. All his life, Gandhi worked tirelessly against intolerance, violence, and injustice. He helped bring independence and democracy to India. He stood by his principles of truth and nonviolence to make a more just society for India and a better world for all people. The Indian people called him *Mahatma*, which means "great soul," and *Bapu*—"father."

Gandhi's message lived after him. Around the world, champions of human rights still study his ideas and try to use them to help people in their own countries. In the United States, the Reverend Martin Luther King, Jr., once said that Gandhi's words and actions showed him how to use nonviolence to lead the civil rights movement in the 1960s.

"My life is my message," Gandhi once said. "You must be the change you wish to see in the world." ❖

Thurgood Marshall

"Equal Justice Under Law": Thurgood Marshall

by Mara Rockliff

At his school in Baltimore, Maryland, in the early 1900s, Thurgood Marshall may have been one of the smartest boys in class, but he was not exactly well behaved. If he wasn't throwing chalk or teasing girls, he was arguing with teachers. So one day, the principal sent him to the basement with a copy of the United States Constitution and **stern** orders not to come back up till he had memorized a passage.

"Before I left that school," Marshall said many years later, "I knew the whole thing by heart."

Parts of the Constitution, however, confused the young Marshall. For example, the Fourteenth Amendment clearly

....

stern firm and serious

stated that all Americans must be treated equally under the law. But growing up in Baltimore in the 1920s, Marshall knew that they were not.

Like other Southern states at that time, Maryland enforced a strict system of segregation. Everywhere, African Americans were kept apart—on buses and trains, in restaurants, hotels, and schools. Anything from a water fountain to a movie theater or public park might have a sign saying "Whites Only."

Even the United States Supreme Court supported these unjust laws. In 1896, in the case of *Plessy v. Ferguson*, the Court had ruled that segregation was allowed under the Constitution: the **facilities** for black Americans, the Court said, simply had to be as good as those for whites— "separate but equal."

In reality, separate almost never meant equal. For example, while Marshall earned high grades in college, the all-white law school of the University of Maryland refused to admit him. (Maryland had no law school for African Americans.) Determined to become a lawyer anyway, he enrolled instead at Howard University in Washington, D.C., one of the few institutions that welcomed African Americans as students.

Marshall left law school eager to win justice for his people. Back in Baltimore, he became known as "the little

....

facilities buildings and resources

man's lawyer," often taking on cases without being paid. Soon, the National Association for the Advancement of Colored People (NAACP) asked him to join their legal team. He took charge, becoming known as "Mr. Civil Rights." He helped organize a **boycott** of businesses that refused to hire African Americans. He successfully sued local school boards that paid black teachers less than half as much as white teachers. He even won a case against the University of Maryland—and the result of the decision was that the university had to admit its first black law student.

In 1950, a group of African American parents in Clarendon County, South Carolina, asked the NAACP for help. Schools in Clarendon County were separate, and far from equal. White children rode buses to modern brick schools with libraries and playgrounds. Black children walked miles past the white schools to cramped, unheated wooden shacks without enough desks and chairs—or even any bathrooms.

The parents took the all-white school board to court, hoping to win a decent education for their children. But Marshall wanted more. He wanted to persuade the court that segregation was itself wrong, that the whole idea of "separate but equal" was **fundamentally** unjust.

To show that segregation made black children feel **inferior**, Marshall brought in a respected psychologist

....

boycott to protest by refusing to buy from or deal with
fundamentally in the most centrally important way
inferior less worthy

named Kenneth Clark. Clark described a simple test he had performed on more than two hundred African American children in segregated schools. He showed each child two white dolls and two brown dolls. Then he asked which dolls they liked best. The children said the white dolls were "nice" and "pretty." The brown dolls, they said, were "ugly" and "dirty." When Clark asked one little girl which doll was most like her, she burst into tears.

Despite Clark's dramatic testimony, and other evidence that Marshall presented, the court ruled that Clarendon County could satisfy the law by spending money to improve black schools. In other words, the court allowed the schools to remain separate, and only required that the county spend more money to make them equal. According to this ruling, segregation was still legal.

Marshall was disappointed, but he was not discouraged. He had a new plan—to take the fight against school segregation to the Supreme Court of the United States.

Marshall and his team of lawyers began gathering cases. One was the Clarendon County case. Others came from Virginia, Kansas, Delaware, and Washington, D.C. The whole group of cases was known by the name of the first scheduled to be heard: *Brown v. Board of Education of Topeka, Kansas.*

Marshall faced opposition even within the African American community. Some said that America was not ready for desegregation. "If you challenge 'separate but equal,'" they said, "we might lose even what we have already gained."

Others supported Marshall. "We want our rights now, not a century **hence**," they said.

Marshall worked tirelessly on the case, hardly stopping to eat or sleep. Finally, on a cold December morning in 1952, Marshall stood looking up at the Supreme Court building. High above him, giant letters carved into the white marble spelled out "Equal Justice Under Law." On this cold day, he hoped he would help those words become reality.

Hundreds of spectators, black and white, crowded the steps. Inside, hundreds more jammed the halls leading to the packed courtroom.

Marshall's opponent was a well-known lawyer named John W. Davis. Marshall greatly admired Davis. As a law student, he had sometimes skipped class to see Davis argue cases before the Supreme Court. Davis seemed unbeatable.

Marshall repeated the argument he had made in South Carolina. Segregation hurt black children. There was no reason for it, other than to keep one race up and the other down. African Americans were not receiving equal treatment under the law.

Davis argued that since the case of *Plessy v. Ferguson*, the Supreme Court had upheld the idea of "separate but

....

hence from now; in the future

equal." Segregation was a fact of Southern life. Why, asked Davis, would black parents want their children in a school where they would be rejected or hated?

In the South, Marshall responded, he had seen white and black children walking down the road together. "They separate and go to different schools," he said, "and they come out and they play together." In other words, children did not choose segregation. They would learn to accept integrated schools.

Davis remained confident. On his way out of the courtroom, he whispered to a **colleague**, "I think we've got it won."

An exhausted Marshall thought so too. As always, Davis had argued with great skill and poise. And the law was on his side. Marshall had little hope that the Supreme Court would admit that they had been wrong for so many years.

But six months passed, and no decision came. Instead, the Court asked the lawyers on both sides for more information. What, they asked, was the original **intent** of the Fourteenth Amendment to the Constitution? That amendment says, "No state shall make or enforce any law which shall **abridge** the privileges or **immunities** of

....

colleague a coworker
intent aim; purpose; goal
abridge to take away from; to cut from
immunities protections

citizens of the United States; nor shall any state ... deny to any person ... the equal protection of the laws." The Supreme Court wanted to know: Does that language allow separation of the races? Does the Court have the power to outlaw school segregation?

It was a second chance. Marshall gathered eighty-five experts—historians, **sociologists**, educators—to help him prepare his answer. Week after week, they planned, talked, and argued together late into the night.

At last, the day arrived. Marshall was ready. In a voice that boomed off the high ceiling of the crowded room, he made his case. Segregation, he argued, was unconstitutional. What reason could there be for separating the two races, he asked, unless the Court found "that for some reason Negroes are inferior to all other human beings"?

As he spoke, Marshall seemed to embody the very point he was arguing. He was knowledgeable, well-spoken, a brilliant lawyer—and African American. Clearly, race had nothing to do with intelligence.

After this second round of arguments was finished, again the months dragged by with no decision from the Court. Marshall went back on the road for the NAACP, trying to raise money to pay the organization's enormous legal bills.

···

sociologists scholars who study the way people function in society

Then, one night in May, after a fundraiser in Mobile, Alabama, the phone rang. Marshall was scheduled to speak in Los Angeles the next day. "Catch the next flight to Washington, D.C.," the caller said—"the Supreme Court is ready to announce its decision."

By early afternoon of the next day, Marshall found himself seated, **shifting** nervously, in the lawyers' section of the Supreme Court.

Chief Justice Earl Warren began to read the Court's opinion. It was long and detailed. He discussed the history of segregation. He gave the legal background. He talked about the importance of education.

Thurgood Marshall standing outside the Supreme Court building, 1955

Which way had the Court decided? Marshall couldn't tell. He stared at one of the justices, a Southerner. Marshall was sure he would fight for segregation. The justice stared back.

....

shifting moving from side to side

Finally, Chief Justice Warren got to the heart of the matter. Did sending black children to separate schools, no matter how good those schools might be, deprive them of an equal opportunity for education?

Warren concluded, "We believe that it does." To separate some children from others for no reason but skin color, he went on, could "affect their hearts and minds in a way unlikely ever to be undone."

The decision was unanimous. All nine justices agreed: Separate schools could never be equal. Segregation must go.

Marshall said later, "I was so happy I was numb."

Over the course of his career with the NAACP, Thurgood Marshall argued 32 cases before the Supreme Court. He won all but three. And in 1967, President Lyndon Johnson appointed him to the Supreme Court, where he served for 24 years. But to many, *Brown v. Board of Education* remained his greatest victory.

A fellow Supreme Court justice said of Marshall, "No American did more to lead our country out of the wilderness of segregation." ❖

On the Front Lines with Thurgood Marshall

an interview with Jack Greenberg
courtesy of the U.S. Department of State

Jack Greenberg was a 27-year-old lawyer in 1954 when he worked with Thurgood Marshall on the Brown v. Board of Education *case, where the Supreme Court ruled that racial segregation was unconstitutional. In this interview, Greenberg shares his thoughts on the* **legacy** *of Thurgood Marshall.*
A professor of law at Columbia University in New York City, Greenberg is the author of several books, including Crusaders in the Courts: Legal Battles of the Civil Rights Movement *(2004). This interview is taken from the U.S. Department of State publication* Justice for All: The Legacy of Thurgood Marshall.

Alexandra Abboud, a staff editor with the U.S. State Department's Bureau of International Information Programs, conducted the interview with Mr. Greenberg.

QUESTION: What would you say was the historical and social **significance** of the 1954 *Brown v. Board of Education* decision?

MR. GREENBERG: *Brown* was a school segregation case that said that the laws in place in the Southern part of the

....

legacy an achievement that continues to exist
significance importance

United States which **prohibited** blacks and whites from going to school together were unconstitutional. But more importantly, the *Brown* case was like an ice breaker going through the frozen sea of racism. It broke up the racist system that was essentially **congealed** into the American polity. We had Southern senators who were elected by whites only, and they kept becoming elected and reelected, and their power depended upon them excluding blacks from political participation. The *Brown* case broke all that up.

QUESTION: What were some of Thurgood Marshall's strengths as an attorney that helped win the *Brown* case?

MR. GREENBERG: Thurgood Marshall was focused. He always believed in racial **integration** and wanted to strike down the segregation laws and practices within the United States. I would liken him to General George Marshall during the Second World War. He was the one who got all the troops together from all different areas, competencies, and abilities and melded them into a focused unit.

We worked with law professors and practitioners, social psychologists, and historians. He was like the orchestra conductor who brought everyone together and focused them into a single melody.

....

prohibited banned or stopped by law
congealed hardened
integration allowing people of all races access to any place

Linda Brown in class at Monroe Elementary

QUESTION: The *Plessy v. Ferguson* case in 1896 resulted in the "separate but equal doctrine," which said that segregation of blacks and whites was legal as long as the separate facilities were of equal quality. In the *Brown* case, Marshall made the argument for the first time that "separate," by definition, could not be equal. Could you explain how Marshall and his legal team decided that it was time to make the challenge with *Brown*?

MR. GREENBERG: In 1935, there was a Maryland state case involving the admission of a black student to the University of Maryland Law School that Marshall won. The student was admitted because there was no law school for blacks. That case never even went to the Supreme Court; it was won in the Maryland state courts. In 1939 there was a case in Missouri which went to the U.S. Supreme Court, and the University of Missouri was ordered to admit a black to the University of Missouri Law School because there was no comparable facility for blacks within the state of Missouri.

Then in 1950 there were two cases, one out of Texas and one from Oklahoma. As the Texas case proceeded, the state, seeing the handwriting on the wall, built a law school for blacks. It had two rooms, didn't have a law library, didn't have a law review, had no **alumni**, but the state argued that was equal, which was a ridiculous claim. And the Supreme Court ruled that there is a lot more than just books, bricks, and the mortar involved in evaluating education. There are the **intangibles** of your relationships with other students and what you learn from them and the lifelong associations that you make while in school.

In the other case, a black student was **excluded** from the University of Oklahoma Graduate School of Education. As the case went on, they didn't build another school for him; instead they allowed him to sit in the back of the room just outside the door and look in. Ultimately, he was admitted into the classroom and to a seat which was marked for "Negroes only." And the Supreme Court said

alumni people who were students of a college or university
intangibles qualities that cannot be measured or touched
excluded purposely prevented someone to be involved

that (action) separated him from the others in a way that interfered with his ability to learn.

So the court was moving more and more towards recognizing the intangible aspects of education and saying that no matter what you did, you could not be equal so long as you were keeping people separate.

In the *Brown* case, the **momentum** of those earlier cases, or the implication of those cases, was made explicit; separate never could be equal.

QUESTION: What is the historical legacy of the Legal Defense Fund at the NAACP?

MR. GREENBERG: The work of the LDF showed that law could accomplish a great deal. It was the first **public-interest law** firm and it institutionalized public-interest law. It won decisions in the Supreme Court saying that the practice of public-interest law is a constitutional right and brought an end to racial segregation. Today, we have this great **proliferation** of public-interest law firms all over the country, which represent a wide variety of political and social issues.

QUESTION: You're a professor at Columbia University Law School. Are there many students today interested in practicing civil rights law?

....

momentum progress that is moving faster
public-interest law legal services that benefit the community
proliferation sudden growth in number

MR. GREENBERG: An enormous number of students are still interested in practicing public-interest law. When I first came to Columbia University, I started a public-interest law program that offers public-interest **fellowships** and internships during the summer. The program now enrolls hundreds of students. In fact, there's so much interest in public-interest law, there's not enough room to accommodate all who really want to be in it. ❖

---

fellowships positions at a university

President John F. Kennedy's Speech at Rice University

September 12, 1962
Houston, Texas

William Bradford, speaking in 1630 of the founding of the Plymouth Bay Colony, said that all great and honorable actions are accompanied with great difficulties, and both must be enterprised and overcome with answerable courage.

If this capsule history of our progress teaches us anything, it is that man, in his quest for knowledge and progress, is determined and cannot be deterred. The exploration of space will go ahead, whether we join in it or not, and it is one of the great adventures of all time, and no nation which expects to be the leader of other nations can expect to stay behind in the race for space.

Those who came before us made certain that this country rode the first waves of the industrial revolutions, the first waves of modern invention, and the first wave of nuclear power, and this generation does not intend to **founder** in the backwash of the coming age of space. We mean to be a part of it—we mean to lead it. For the eyes of the world now look into space, to the moon, and to the

....

founder to fail

planets beyond, and we have vowed that we shall not see it governed by a hostile flag of conquest, but by a banner of freedom and peace. We have vowed that we shall not see space filled with weapons of mass destruction, but with instruments of knowledge and understanding.

Yet the vows of this Nation can only be fulfilled if we in this Nation are first, and, therefore, we intend to be first. In short, our leadership in science and in industry, our hopes for peace and security, our **obligations** to ourselves as well as others, all require us to make this effort, to solve these mysteries, to solve them for the good of all men, and to become the world's leading space-faring nation.

We set sail on this new sea because there is new knowledge to be gained, and new rights to be won, and they must be won and used for the progress of all people. For space science, like nuclear science and all technology, has no conscience of its own. Whether it will become a force for good or ill depends on man, and only if the United States occupies a position of **preeminence** can we help decide whether this new ocean will be a sea of peace or a new terrifying theater of war. I do not say the we should or will go unprotected against the hostile misuse of space any more than we go unprotected against the hostile use of land or sea, but I do say that space can be explored and mastered without feeding the fires of war, without

obligations duties
preeminence importance

President John F. Kennedy speaking at Rice University

repeating the mistakes that man has made in extending his writ around this globe of ours.

There is no strife, no prejudice, no national conflict in outer space as yet. Its **hazards** are hostile to us all. Its conquest deserves the best of all mankind, and its opportunity for peaceful cooperation many never come again. But why, some say, the moon? Why choose this as our goal? And they may well ask why climb the highest mountain? Why, 35 years ago, fly the Atlantic? Why does Rice play Texas?

....

hazards dangers

We choose to go to the moon. We choose to go to the moon in this decade and do the other things, not because they are easy, but because they are hard, because that goal will serve to organize and measure the best of our energies and skills, because that challenge is one that we are willing to accept, one we are unwilling to **postpone**, and one which we intend to win, and the others, too.

It is for these reasons that I regard the decision last year to shift our efforts in space from low to high gear as among the most important decisions that will be made during my incumbency in the office of the Presidency. ❖

---

postpone to delay

First Lady Michelle Obama's Remarks in Town Hall with Youth of Northern Ireland

June 17, 2013
Belfast Waterfront, Northern Ireland

It is such a pleasure to be here in **Belfast**. And as you might imagine, whenever we travel to places like this or anywhere else in the world, we've got a pretty packed schedule. We're meeting with Presidents and Prime Ministers and First Ladies. We're visiting historical sites and attending state dinners. And my husband is spending hours trying to make progress on global issues from trade to international security.

But wherever we go, no matter what's on our plate, we always do our best to meet with young people just like all of you. In fact, you all might just very well be some of the most important people that we talk to during our visits, because in just a couple of decades, you will be the ones in charge. Yes, indeed. You'll be the ones shaping our shared future with your passion and energy and ideas.

So when I look around this room, I don't just see a bunch of teenagers. I see the people who will be moving

Belfast a city in Northern Ireland

our world forward in the years ahead. And that's why we wanted to be here today.

Let me tell you, when I was your age, I never dreamed that I'd be standing here as First Lady of the United States. And I know that my husband never thought he'd be President, either. Neither of us grew up with much money. Neither of my parents went to university. Barack's father left his family when Barack was just two years old. He was raised by a single mom.

And all along the way, there were plenty of people who doubted that kids like us had what it took to succeed—people who told us not to hope for too much or set our sights too high.

But Barack and I refused to let other people define us. Instead, we held tight to those values we were raised with—things like honesty, hard work, a commitment to our education.

We did our best to be open to others; to give everyone we met a fair shake, no matter who they were or where they came from. And we soon realized that the more we lived by those values, the more we'd see them from other people in return. We saw that when we reached out and listened to somebody else's **perspective**, that person was more likely to listen to us. If we treated a classmate with respect, they'd treat us well in return.

....

perspective attitude, viewpoint

Michelle Obama addressing the audience at Waterfront Hall

And that's sort of how we became who we are today. That's how we learned what leadership really means. It's about stepping outside of your comfort zone to explore new ideas. It's about rising above old divisions. It's about treating people the way you want to be treated in return.

And as young people, you all are in a very powerful position to make some of those same choices yourselves. You have the freedom of an open mind. You have a fresh perspective that can help you find solutions to age-old problems. And with today's technology, you can connect with other young people from all over Northern Ireland and all around the world.

So right now, you've got a choice to make. You've got to decide how you're going to use those advantages and opportunities to build the lives you dream of. Because that decision will determine not only the kinds of people you'll become, but also the kinds of communities you'll live in, the kind of world we'll all share together.

And standing here with all of you today, I have never felt more **optimistic**, let me tell you. Because time and again, I have seen young people like all of you choosing to work together, choosing to lift each other up, choosing to leave behind the conflicts and **prejudices** of the past and create a bright future for us all.

That's what's so powerful about your generation. And again, that's why we're here today—because we want you to know that we believe in each and every one of you. That is exactly why we're here. We believe that you all have the ability to make a mark on this world that will last for generations to come. We are so proud of you. We expect great things. ❖

---

optimistic hopeful about the future
prejudices predetermined opinions not based on experience or reason

Human Kindness

Before Giving to a Charity

from Federal Trade Commission

You want your donations to count. That's why it's important to ask questions whenever you're asked to give— whether over the phone, in direct mail, or online. Do some research before donating. You should know, for example, exactly how much of your donation goes to the program you want to support. Don't donate until you're sure it will make a difference. Here are some things you can do to make sure your donations get where they'll do good—and help you avoid donating to a scam.

If you want to give to charity:

- Search online for the cause you care about—like "hurricane relief" or "homeless kids"—plus phrases like "best charity" or "highly rated charity." Once you find a specific charity you're considering giving to, search its name plus "complaint," "review," "rating," or "scam." If you find **red flags**, it might be best to find another organization.

- Check out the charity's website. Does it give information about the programs you want to support, or how it uses donations? How much of your donation will go directly to support the programs you care about? If you can't find detailed information about a charity's mission and programs, be suspicious.

- Use one of these organizations to help you research charities: BBB Wise Giving Alliance, Charity Navigator, CharityWatch, and GuideStar.

Federal Trade Commission 2019

....

red flags warning signs

- See what your state's charity regulator has to say about the charity. Don't know who that is? Look it up at nasconet.org (http://www.nasconet.org/resources/state-government/).

- Before you donate through an online portal that lets you choose from a list of charities, read the article "Donating Through an Online Giving Portal" (https://www.consumer.ftc.gov/articles/donating-through-online-giving-portal), available at FTC.gov/Charity. It explains how these online giving portals work.

If you get a call from a fundraiser:

- You don't have to give over the phone. Don't let any caller pressure you. A legitimate charity will be happy to get your donation at any time, so there's no rush. Take time to do the research.

- Ask the fundraiser for the charity's exact name, web address, and mailing address, so you can confirm it later. Some dishonest telemarketers use names that sound like large well-known charities to confuse you.

- Ask how much of your donation will go directly to the program you want to help. Then, call the organization directly and ask them, too, or see if the information is on their website. What else does the charity spend money on? Some fundraising can be very expensive, leaving the charity with little money to spend on its programs.

- Ask if your donation will be **tax-deductible**. Not every call seeking a donation is from a charity. Some calls might be from Political Action Committees or other groups where donations are not deductible. You can make sure that your donation is to a charity and tax-deductible by looking up the organization in the IRS's Tax Exempt Organization Search (https://www.irs.gov/charities-non-profits/tax-exempt-organization-search).

- Check to see if the fundraiser and charity are registered with your state's charity regulator (if that's required in your state [https://www.nasconet.org/resources/state-government/]).

If you get a donation request through social media or a crowdfunding site:

- Keep in mind that crowdfunding sites often have little control over who uses them and how donations are spent. Research any charity before you give. Also, if tax deductions are important to you, remember that donations to individuals are not tax deductible.

- The safest way to give on social media or through crowdfunding is to donate to people you know who contact you about a specific project. Don't assume **solicitations** on social media or crowdfunding sites are

---

tax-deductible subtract the amount of the donation from taxable income
solicitations requests for donations

legitimate, or that hyperlinks are accurate—even in posts that are shared or liked by your friends. Do your own research. Call your friends or contact them offline to ask them about the post they shared.

- You can always go directly to a charity's website and donate directly that way.

If you're ready to donate:

- Be careful how you pay. If someone asks you to pay by giving them the numbers from a gift card, or by wiring money, don't do it. That's how scammers ask you to pay. It's safest to pay by credit card or check—and only after you have done some research on the charity.

- If someone wants you to leave your donation in cash under your doormat, be suspicious. You're probably dealing with a scammer.

After you've donated:

- Review your bank account and credit card statements closely to make sure you're only charged the amount you agreed to donate—and that you're not signed up to make a **recurring** donation.

- It's a good practice to keep a record of all donations.

....

legitimate trustworthy
recurring happening again multiple times

How to avoid donating to a sham charity:

- Don't let anyone rush you into making a donation. That's something scammers do.

- Don't feel pressured to donate. Scammers will say anything to get you to give them money. They may say you already **pledged** to make the donation, or that you donated to them last year. They may even send you a mailer that says you already pledged. Don't let that pressure you into paying what could be a scammer.

- Don't trust your caller ID. Technology makes it easy for scammers to have caller ID say the call comes from anywhere, including your local area code, or from a particular name. In reality, the caller could be anywhere in the world. If you want your donation to help your local community, ask questions about where your donation will be used and how much of your donation will be spent there.

- Check out the name of the charity, especially if it sounds like a well-known organization. Some scammers use names that sound a lot like other charities to trick you.

- Watch out for solicitations that give lots of vague and sentimental claims, but give you no specifics about how your donation will be used.

pledged promised

- If someone is guaranteeing you sweepstakes winnings in exchange for a contribution, that's a scam.

How to handle calls from telemarketers:

Even if your number is on the National Do Not Call Registry, the Telemarketing Sales Rule lets fundraisers asking for charitable solicitations to call you until you tell them to stop. To do that, ask to be placed on the charity's do not call list. Fundraisers who call you have to follow other rules too:

- They can't call you before 8 a.m. or after 9 p.m.

- They have to tell you the name of the charity they're calling for and tell you if the purpose of the call is to seek a donation.

- They can't deceive you or lie about:
  - The fundraiser's connection to the charity.
  - The mission or purpose of the charity.
  - Whether a donation is tax deductible.
  - How a donation will be used, or how much of the donation actually goes to the charity's programs.
  - The charity's affiliation with the government.

- They can't use a robocall or prerecorded message to reach you unless you have supported the charity in the past.

- The caller ID on your phone has to show the name of the charity or fundraiser, along with a number that you can call to ask to be placed on the charity's do not call list.

  If a fundraiser breaks any of these rules, that's a red flag. Do some more research before you donate to them. If you think you've been contacted by a scam charity, or a fundraiser that is not following the rules, please tell the FTC: FTC.gov/Complaint (http://www.ftc.gov/Complaint). It's most helpful to tell the FTC the name of the charity or fundraiser and why you think it was a scam. ❖

Operation Donate with Honor

poster from Federal Trade Commission

Operation
★
Donate with Honor

Which veterans group would you donate to?

American Disabled Veterans Foundation

National Vietnam Veterans Foundation

Healing American Heroes, Inc.

Veterans Fighting Breast Cancer

Military Families of America

VietNow National Headquarters, Inc.

Foundation for American Veterans, Inc.

Healing Heroes Network

Help the Vets, Inc.

They have all been sued for lying to donors.

**Don't depend on the name.
Do your research.
Then donate.**

ftc.gov/charity

Thank You, M'am

by Langston Hughes

She was a large woman with a large purse that had everything in it but a hammer and nails. It had a long strap, and she carried it slung across her shoulder. It was about eleven o'clock at night, dark, and she was walking alone, when a boy ran up behind her and tried to snatch her purse. The strap broke with the sudden single tug the boy gave it from behind. But the boy's weight and the weight of the purse combined caused him to lose his balance. Instead of taking off full blast as he had hoped, the boy fell on his back on the sidewalk and his legs flew up. The large woman simply turned around and kicked him right square in his blue-jeaned sitter. Then she reached down, picked the boy up by his shirt front, and shook him until his teeth rattled.

After that the woman said, "Pick up my pocketbook, boy, and give it here."

She still held him tightly. But she bent down enough to permit him to stoop and pick up her purse. Then she said, "Now ain't you ashamed of yourself?"

Firmly gripped by his shirt front, the boy said, "Yes'm."

The woman said, "What did you want to do it for?"

The boy said, "I didn't aim to."

She said, "You a lie!"

By that time two or three people passed, stopped, turned to look, and some stood watching.

"If I turn you loose, will you run?" asked the woman.

"Yes'm," said the boy.

"Then I won't turn you loose," said the woman. She did not release him.

"Lady, I'm sorry," whispered the boy.

"Um-hum! Your face is dirty. I got a great mind to wash your face for you. Ain't you got nobody home to tell you to wash your face?"

"No'm," said the boy.

"Then it will get washed this evening," said the large woman, starting up the street, dragging the frightened boy behind her.

He looked as if he were fourteen or fifteen, frail and willow-wild, in tennis shoes and blue jeans.

The woman said, "You ought to be my son. I would teach you right from wrong. Least I can do right now is to wash your face. Are you hungry?"

"No'm," said the being-dragged boy. "I just want you to turn me loose."

"Was I bothering you when I turned that corner?" asked the woman.

"No'm."

"But you put yourself in contact with me?" said the woman. "If you think that that contact is not going to last awhile, you got another thought coming. When I get

through with you, sir, you are going to remember
Mrs. Luella Bates Washington Jones."

Sweat popped out on the boy's face and he began to
struggle. Mrs. Jones stopped, jerked him around in front
of her, put a half nelson about his neck, and continued
to drag him up the street. When she got to her door, she
dragged the boy inside, down a hall, and into a large
kitchenette-furnished room at the rear of the house. She
switched on the light and left the door open. The boy could
hear other roomers laughing and talking in the large
house. Some of their doors were open, too, so he knew he
and the woman were not alone. The woman still had him
by the neck in the middle of her room.

She said, "What is your name?"

"Roger," answered the boy.

"Then, Roger, you go to that sink and wash your face,"
said the woman, whereupon she turned him loose—at last.
Roger looked at the door—looked at the woman—looked at
the door—and went to the sink.

"Let the water run until it gets warm," she said. "Here's
a clean towel."

"You gonna take me to jail?" asked the boy, bending
over the sink.

"Not with that face, I would not take you nowhere,"
said the woman. "Here I am trying to get home to cook me
a bite to eat, and you snatch my pocketbook! Maybe you
ain't been to your supper either, late as it be. Have you?"

"There's nobody home at my house," said the boy.

"Then we'll eat," said the woman. "I believe you're hungry—or been hungry—to try to snatch my pocketbook!"

"I want a pair of blue suede shoes," said the boy.

"Well, you didn't have to snatch my pocketbook to get some suede shoes," said Mrs. Luella Bates Washington Jones. "You could of asked me."

"M'am?"

The water dripping from his face, the boy looked at her. There was a long pause. A very long pause. After he had dried his face and not knowing what else to do, dried it again, the boy turned around, wondering what next. The door was open. He could make a dash for it down the hall. He could run, run, run, *run*!

The woman was sitting on the daybed. After a while she said, "I were young once and I wanted things I could not get."

There was another long pause. The boy's mouth opened. Then he frowned, not knowing he frowned.

The woman said, "Um-hum! You thought I was going to say *but*, didn't you? You thought I was going to say, *but I didn't snatch people's pocketbooks*. Well, I wasn't going to say that." Pause. Silence. "I have done things, too, which I would

not tell you, son—neither tell God, if He didn't already know. Everybody's got something in common. So you set down while I fix us something to eat. You might run that comb through your hair so you will look **presentable**."

In another corner of the room behind a screen was a gas plate and an icebox. Mrs. Jones got up and went behind the screen. The woman did not watch the boy to see if he was going to run now, nor did she watch her purse, which she left behind her on the daybed. But the boy took care to sit on the far side of the room, away from the purse, where he thought she could easily see him out of the corner of her eye if she wanted to. He did not trust the woman not to trust him. And he did not want to be mistrusted now.

"Do you need somebody to go to the store," asked the boy, "maybe to get some milk or something?"

"Don't believe I do," said the woman, "unless you just want sweet milk yourself. I was going to make cocoa out of this canned milk I got here."

"That will be fine," said the boy.

She heated some lima beans and ham she had in the icebox, made the cocoa, and set the table. The woman did not ask the boy anything about where he lived, or his folks, or anything else that would embarrass him. Instead, as they ate, she told him about her job in a hotel beauty shop that stayed open late, what the work was like, and how all

....

presentable worthy of being seen by others

kinds of women came in and out, blondes, redheads, and Spanish. Then she cut him a half of her ten-cent cake.

"Eat some more, son," she said.

When they were finished eating, she got up and said, "Now here, take this ten dollars and buy yourself some blue suede shoes. And next time, do not make the mistake of latching onto my pocketbook nor nobody else's—because shoes got by devilish ways will burn your feet. I got to get my rest now. But from here on in, son, I hope you will behave yourself."

She led him down the hall to the front door and opened it. "Good night! Behave yourself, boy!" she said, looking out into the street as he went down the steps.

The boy wanted to say something other than, "Thank you, m'am," to Mrs. Luella Bates Washington Jones, but although his lips moved, he couldn't even say that as he turned at the foot of the **barren** stoop and looked up at the large woman in the door. Then she shut the door. ❖

....

barren bare

An Hour with Abuelo

by Judith Ortiz Cofer

"Just one hour, *una hora*, is all I'm asking of you, son."
My grandfather is in a nursing home in Brooklyn, and my
mother wants me to spend some time with him, since the
doctors say that he doesn't have too long to go now. *I* don't
have much time left of my summer vacation, and there's a
stack of books next to my bed I've got to read if I'm going
to get into the AP English class I want. I'm going stupid
in some of my classes, and Mr. Williams, the principal at
Central, said that if I passed some reading tests, he'd let
me move up.

Besides, I hate the place, the old people's home, especially the way it smells like industrial-strength ammonia and other stuff I won't mention, since it turns my stomach. And really the **abuelo** always has a lot of relatives visiting him, so I've gotten out of going out there except at Christmas, when a whole vanload of grandchildren are herded over there to give him gifts and a hug. We all make it quick and spend the rest of the time in the recreation area, where they play checkers and stuff with some of the old people's games, and I catch up on back issues of *Modern Maturity*. I'm not picky, I'll read almost anything.

Anyway, after my mother nags me for about a week, I let her drive me to Golden Years. She drops me off in front. She wants me to go in alone and have a "good time" talking to Abuelo. I tell her to be back in one hour or I'll take the bus back to Patterson. She squeezes my hand and says, "*Gracias*, *hijo*," in a choked-up voice like I'm doing her a big favor.

I get depressed the minute I walk into the place. They line up the old people in wheelchairs in the hallway as if they were about to be raced to the finish line by orderlies who don't even look at them when they push them here and there. I walk fast to room 10, Abuelo's "suite." He is sitting up in his bed writing with a pencil in one of those

abuelo grandfather
Gracias, hijo "Thank you, son."

old-fashioned black hardback notebooks. It has the outline of the island of Puerto Rico on it. I slide into the hard vinyl chair by his bed. He sort of smiles and the lines on his face get deeper, but he doesn't say anything. Since I'm supposed to talk to him, I say, "What are you doing, Abuelo, writing the story of your life?"

It's supposed to be a joke, but he answers, "Si, how did you know, Arturo?"

His name is Arturo too. I was named after him. I don't really know my grandfather. His children, including my mother, came to New York and New Jersey (where I was born) and he stayed on the Island until my grandmother died. Then he got sick, and since nobody could leave their jobs to go take care of him, they brought him to this nursing home in Brooklyn. I see him a couple of times a year, but he's always surrounded by his sons and daughters. My mother tells me that **Don** Arturo had once been a teacher back in Puerto Rico, but had lost his job after the war. Then he became a farmer. She's always saying in a sad voice, "Ay, bandito! What a waste of a fine mind." Then she usually shrugs her shoulders and says, "*Asi es la vida.*" That's the way life is. It sometimes makes me mad that the adults I know just accept whatever is thrown at them because "that's the way things are." Not for me. I go after what I want.

....

Don a Spanish title of respect, used before a man's name

Anyway, Abuelo is looking at me like he was trying to see into my head, but he doesn't say anything. Since I like stories, I decide I may as well ask him if he'll read me what he wrote.

I look at my watch; I've already used up twenty minutes of the hour I promised my mother.

Abuelo starts talking in his slow way. He speaks what my mother calls book English. He taught himself from a dictionary, and his words sound stiff, like he's sounding them out in his head before he says them. With his children he speaks Spanish, and that funny book English with us grandchildren. I'm surprised that he's still so sharp, because his body is shrinking like a crumpled-up brown paper sack with some bones in it. But I can see from looking into his eyes that the light is still on in there.

"It is a short story, Arturo. The story of my life. It will not take very much time to read it."

"I have time, Abuelo." I'm a little embarrassed that he saw me looking at my watch.

"Yes, hijo. You have spoken the truth. *La verdad*. You have much time."

Abuelo reads: "'I loved words from the beginning of my life. In the **campo** where I was born one of seven sons, there were few books. My mother read them to us over and over: the Bible, the stories of Spanish conquistadors and of

---

campo countryside

pirates that she had read as a child and brought with her from the city of Mayaguez; that was before she married my father, a coffee bean farmer; and she taught us words from the newspaper that a boy on a horse brought every week to her. She taught each of us how to write on a slate with chalks that she ordered by mail every year. We used those chalks until they were so small that you lost them between your fingers.

"'I always wanted to be a writer and a teacher. With my heart and my soul I knew that I wanted to be around books all of my life. And so against the wishes of my father, who wanted all his sons to help him on the land, she sent me to high school in Mayaguez. For four years I boarded with a couple she knew. I paid my rent in labor, and I ate vegetables I grew myself. I wore my clothes until they were thin as parchment. But I graduated at the top of my class! My whole family came to see me that day. My mother brought me a beautiful *guayabera*, a white shirt made of the finest cotton and embroidered by her own hands. I was a happy young man.

"'In those days you could teach in a country school with a high school diploma. So I went back to my mountain village and got a job teaching all grades in a little classroom built by the parents of my students.

"'I had books sent to me by the government. I felt like a rich man although the pay was very small. I had books. All the books I wanted! I taught my students how to read poetry and plays, and how to write them. We made up songs and put on shows for the parents. It was a beautiful time for me.

"'Then the war came, and the American President said that all Puerto Rican men would be drafted. I wrote to our governor and explained that I was the only teacher in the mountain village. I told him that the children would go back to the fields and grow up ignorant if I could not teach them their letters. I said that I thought I was a better teacher than a soldier. The governor did not answer my letter. I went into the U.S. Army.

"'I told my sergeant that I could be a teacher in the army. I could teach all the farm boys their letters so that they could read the instructions on the ammunition boxes and not blow themselves up. The sergeant said I was too smart for my own good, and gave me a job cleaning latrines. He said to me there is reading material for you there, scholar. Read the writing on the walls. I spent the war mopping floors and cleaning toilets.

"'When I came back to the Island, things had changed. You had to have a college degree to teach school, even the lower grades. My parents were sick, two of my brothers had been killed in the war, the others had stayed in Nueva York. I was the only one left to help the old people. I became a farmer. I married a good woman who gave me many good children. I taught them all how to read and write before they started school.'"

Abuelo then puts the notebook down on his lap and closes his eyes.

"*Asi es la vida* is the title of my book," he says in a whisper, almost to himself. Maybe he's forgotten that I'm there.

For a long time he doesn't say anything else. I think that he's sleeping, but then I see that he's watching me through half-closed lids, maybe waiting for my opinion of his writing. I'm trying to think of something nice to say. I liked it and all, but not the title. And I think that he could've been a teacher if he had wanted to bad enough. Nobody is going to stop me from doing what I want with my life. I'm not going to let *la vida* get in my way. I want to discuss this with him, but the words are not coming into my head in Spanish just yet. I'm about to ask him why he didn't keep fighting to make his dream come true, when an old lady in hot-pink running shoes sort of appears at the door.

She is wearing a pink jogging outfit too. The world's oldest marathoner, I say to myself. She calls out to my grandfather in a flirty voice, "Yoo-hoo, Arturo, remember what day this is? It's poetry-reading day in the rec room! You promised us you'd read your new one today."

I see my abuelo perking up almost immediately. He points to his wheelchair, which is hanging like a huge metal bat in the open closet. He makes it obvious that he wants me to get it. I put it together, and with Mrs. Pink

Running Shoes's help, we get him in it. Then he says in a strong deep voice I hardly recognize, "Arturo, get that notebook from the table, please."

I hand him another map-of-the-Island notebook—this one is red. On it in big letters it says, **_POEMAS DE ARTURO_**.

I start to push him toward the rec room, but he shakes his finger at me.

"Arturo, look at your watch now. I believe your time is over." He gives me a wicked smile.

Then with her pushing the wheelchair—maybe a little too fast—they roll down the hall. He is already reading from his notebook, and she's making bird noises. I look at my watch and the hour is up, to the minute. I can't help but think that my abuelo has been timing me. It cracks me up. I walk slowly down the hall toward the exit sign. I want my mother to have to wait a little. I don't want her to think that I'm in a hurry or anything. ❖

POEMAS DE ARTURO Arturo's Poems

*adapted from statement by
President Barack Obama on*

Malala Yousafzai and Kailash Satyarthi Winning the 2014 Nobel Peace Prize

*October 10, 2014
The White House, Office of the Press Secretary*

On behalf of Michelle, myself and all Americans, I want to congratulate Malala Yousafzai and Kailash Satyarthi on winning the Nobel Peace Prize. This is a victory for all who strive to uphold the **dignity** of every human being. In recognizing Malala and Kailash, the Nobel Committee reminds us of the urgency of their work to protect the rights and freedoms of all our young people. It will ensure young people have the chance to fulfill their God-given potential, regardless of their background, or gender, or station in life.

At just 17 years old, Malala Yousafzai has inspired people around the world with her **passion** and determination to make sure girls everywhere can get an education. When the Taliban tried to silence her, Malala answered their **brutality** with strength and resolve.

....

dignity self-respect
passion strong feeling
brutality violent actions

President Barack Obama, First Lady Michelle Obama, and their daughter Malia Obama meeting with Malala Yousafzai in the Oval Office, October 11, 2013

Michelle and I were proud to welcome this remarkable young woman to the Oval Office last year. We were **awe-struck** by her courage. We were filled with hope knowing this is only the beginning of her extraordinary efforts to make the world a better place.

Kailash Satyarthi has dedicated his life to ending child labor and wiping the stain of slavery from our world. The true measure of Kailash's efforts is not a single prize he has been awarded. It is the tens of thousands of people who today live with freedom and dignity thanks to his efforts.

....

awe-struck filled with wonder; extremely impressed

President Barack Obama meeting with Kailash Satyarthi, as his wife Sumedha Satyarth and First Lady Michelle Obama look on

Through his **advocacy**, Kailash reminds us of our shared responsibility to end the **exploitation** of others, especially the most **vulnerable** among us.

Malala and Kailash have faced down threats and intimidation. They have risked their own lives to save others and build a better world for future generations. They come from different countries, religious backgrounds, and generations—a Muslim and a Hindu, a Pakistani and

advocacy support
exploitation unfair treatment
vulnerable easily hurt

an Indian—but they share an unyielding commitment to justice and an unshakeable belief in the basic dignity of every girl and boy. Even as we celebrate their achievements, we must recommit ourselves to the world that they seek. A world in which our daughters have the right and opportunity to get an education. A world in which all children are treated equally. Today, we honor Malala and Kailash's achievements, and reaffirm that the United States will always stand with those who defend our universal human rights. ❖

Malala the Powerful

by Kristin Lewis
Scholastic Scope, September 2013

October 9, 2012, was an ordinary afternoon in the Swat
Valley, an area of rugged mountains and sweeping green
valleys in north Pakistan. Malala Yousafzai, 15, was sitting
on a school bus with her classmates waiting to go home
when two bearded gunmen appeared.

"Who is Malala?" one of the men demanded. A feeling
of terror filled the bus. And then the unthinkable happened:
The gunmen opened fire. One bullet pierced Malala's head
near her left eye. Two of Malala's friends were struck in
their arms. Then the gunmen fled, leaving Malala to die.
It might be difficult to understand why anyone would try
to murder an innocent girl on her way home from school,
but some people in Pakistan do not view Malala for what
she is: a bright and generous teenager. They see her as a
deadly threat to their way of life, a person who deserves
to be killed. These people—mainly young men from rural
Pakistan and neighboring Afghanistan—are members of
a group called the Taliban. They believe in an extreme
interpretation of Islam that most Muslim people do not
agree with. For years, the Taliban had been plotting to kill
Malala. Why? Because she was not only a 15-year-old girl;

....

interpretation explanation of the meaning

Malala Yousafzai

she was also a **crusader** for girls' right to go to school.
This work had made her famous throughout Pakistan
and around the world. It had also made her a target of
the Taliban.

Life Is Brutal

Malala is from Mingora, a city in the Swat Valley. It's a
gorgeous place, known for its majestic green mountains,
thick forests, and mighty rivers. It was once a popular
vacation spot, attracting tourists from all over the world.
In the past few years, though, it has become a war zone.
Starting in 2007, the Taliban began seizing control of
Swat. When the Pakistani army tried to stop them, the
Taliban responded with tremendous violence. They blew
up government buildings and murdered police officers.
At night, Malala was often awakened by the terrifying

---

crusader someone who works hard on behalf of a cause

sounds of gunfire. During the day, she frequently walked by corpses of men and women executed by the Taliban and left on the street as a warning to those who would dare defy them. The Taliban are not part of Pakistan's government, but their forces are powerful. They operate mostly in Afghanistan and Pakistan. Those who live in areas under Taliban control are forced to follow **oppressive** religious rules. All music is banned. So are television and movies. Democracy is seen as an offense against Islam. For women and girls, life is particularly brutal: They are not allowed to go to school, have careers, or wear makeup or bright clothing. They are not allowed to go anywhere without a male relative. Breaking these rules brings severe punishment, which may include public whipping or even execution. Like most Pakistanis, Malala and her family do not support the Taliban's version of Islam. Malala's family is, in fact, deeply religious, but the Taliban do not tolerate any form of Islam that differs from its own.

School Ban

In January 2009, the Taliban ordered all girls' schools to close. That included Malala's school, which her father had owned for more than a decade. It was **devastating** news. School was one of the most important parts of Malala's life—and a luxury she never took for granted.

oppressive cruel and unfair; treating people unjustly
devastating very upsetting

After all, fewer than half the girls in rural Pakistan had the opportunity to receive any education at all. Despite the Taliban's order, Malala's father decided to keep his school open. This was incredibly dangerous, especially because the Taliban were gaining popularity in Swat. Some residents saw them as a welcome alternative to Pakistan's government and military, which have been plagued by **corruption**. From then on, Malala and her family lived under constant threat. Across the region, hundreds of schools were being bombed. Teachers were being murdered. Malala and her classmates stopped wearing their school uniforms and began hiding their books under their clothing. Staying alive meant going to school had to be top secret. Even with these precautions, many parents felt the risk was too great. Attendance at Malala's school decreased by more than 60 percent. But what could Malala do? What could one girl do but watch helplessly as her freedoms were taken away?

A Powerful Weapon

It turns out, there was something she could do. Malala possessed a weapon of her own: her voice. And she would risk everything to use it. In 2009, she began **blogging** for the British Broadcasting Company's (BBC) Urdu site about what her life was like under the Taliban. (Urdu is an official

corruption dishonest behavior by individuals in an organization
blogging maintaining an online personal journal of thoughts and feelings

language of Pakistan.) To protect her identity, she used a **pseudonym**. She wrote about her dream of becoming a doctor one day, her fears of the terrorists, and her fierce determination to get the education she needed, no matter what the Taliban did or how afraid she was. And indeed, fear was her constant companion. "On my way from school to home I heard a man saying, 'I will kill you,'" she wrote in one blog entry. "I hastened my pace and after a while I looked back [to see] if the man was still coming behind me. But to my utter relief he was talking on his mobile and must have been threatening someone else over the phone." The blog was an instant hit; soon, people all over the world were reading it. Malala was helping to focus attention on what was happening in Swat. Outrage grew, and many in Pakistan and around the world criticized the Pakistani government for allowing the Taliban to become so powerful.

A Crusade

In May 2009, the Pakistani army launched a full-scale attack against the Taliban in Swat. Along with millions of refugees, Malala and her family were evacuated south. The conflict lasted for three months; by August, most of the Taliban had been pushed out of the cities and into the countryside, and it was safe to go home. After that, Malala launched a full-scale attack of her own. She became even bolder in her crusade. Her identity as the famous BBC

pseudonym a false name

blogger was revealed. She appeared in a *New York Times* documentary, went on television shows, and gave powerful speeches to Pakistani kids. Her message was always the same: All children deserve the right to an education. Malala's fears of **retaliation** did not subside, though. When asked on a Pakistani talk show about the dangers of speaking out, she eerily described how the Taliban might come for her one day: "I think of it often and imagine the scene clearly," she said. "Even if they come to kill me, I will tell them what they are trying to do is wrong, that education is our basic right." Malala's crusade empowered her and other girls. Her courage gave hope to thousands. It also made her a star. In 2011, the President of Pakistan awarded her the first ever National Youth Peace Prize. It seemed that everyone knew her name. Including the Taliban.

Attacked

In 2010, notes began appearing under Malala's door, ordering her to give up her crusade or else. But she refused to back down, and on October 9, 2012, Taliban gunmen shot her and two others on the school bus. The hours following the shooting were a nightmare. Malala's friends were not critically injured, but Malala was in bad shape. The bullet had destroyed her left ear and sent fragments of her skull into her brain tissue, but miraculously, she

retaliation revenge for a real or imagined wrong

clung to life. She was flown to a hospital in Birmingham, in the United Kingdom, that specializes in traumatic brain injuries. Her family soon joined her. The Taliban soon took credit for the assassination attempt, saying it was a warning to other girls not to follow Malala's example. Meanwhile, the world waited, tense and furious. The United Nations Special Envoy for Global Education immediately started a petition, calling on the President of Pakistan to make a place in school for every girl. Soon 1 million people had signed. Cards flooded Malala's hospital room. In Pakistan, millions lifted up prayers for her. Candlelight vigils were held across the globe. Protesters marched, many of them kids carrying signs that read "I Am Malala." It seemed that by trying to silence her, the Taliban had unwittingly helped thousands more find a voice of their own.

To Serve Humanity

It's been nearly a year since the shooting, and in many ways, Malala's life has changed dramatically. The bullet severely damaged her hearing and fractured her skull, causing her brain to swell dangerously. Fortunately, the physicians in Birmingham were able to control the swelling. Over the past months, she has undergone several operations to repair her skull and improve her hearing. In the meantime, Malala's father has been given a job that enables the family to remain in the U.K., where, hopefully, they will be safe from the Taliban, who have vowed to come after Malala again. Today, Malala has become a powerful symbol of the struggle so many kids face. Some 132 million children and teens around the world do not attend school, often because they must work to help support their families or because they have no school to go to. Malala hopes to change that. She envisions a world in which all children, and especially girls, can get the education they need to become whatever they want—from doctors and scientists to politicians and journalists. In one of her first public statements after the shooting, Malala stated that she felt her role was to "serve humanity." This fall, she will publish a memoir. The Malala Fund, created in her name, is helping to send 40 girls in Pakistan to school. (For their protection, the girls' names and the name and location of the school have not been disclosed.) There is talk that Malala should run for President someday.

For now, though, she is getting the one thing she has always wanted. Last March, she started high school in Birmingham. On her first day, she addressed a news crew. There were signs that she had not yet fully recovered— her mouth drooped slightly when she spoke and there were scars on the side of her face. But her voice was clear, her eyes shining. She pointed to her jacket. "Today, I am wearing a uniform," she said proudly. "It is important, because it proves that I am a student. It is the happiest day for me because I am living my life, I am going to school, I am learning." ❖

The Strangers That Came to Town

by Ambrose Flack

The first of April was dark and stormy. Silver whips of lightning were cracking open low-hanging clouds. My brother Tom and I were recovering from chest colds. Tired of listening to the radio, we turned to the big living-room window of our house on Syringa Street.

"Here they come, Mother," yelled Tom when a truck drove up in the rain and stopped at the empty cottage across the street.

Mother hurried in from the kitchen, and we three looked out. That truck, we knew, contained the Duvitch family and all their earthly possessions.

All afternoon Mother, Tom, and I had been watching for them with mixed emotions. For the Duvitches had just come over from Europe, and they were the first of the nationality to settle in our town.

A stream of children, accompanied by a big brown dog, poured out of the back of the truck and stood in a huddle in the rain. Mr. Duvitch and the biggest boy carefully helped Mrs. Duvitch from the seat and walked her into the house.

"I wonder if Mrs. Duvitch is ill," murmured Mother.

"She must be," said Tom. "I wonder if it would be all right for Andy and me to help them move in their stuff."

Mother shook her head. It was a strict family rule that any illness which kept us out of school also kept us indoors.

Yet the Duvitches got along very well without help from us. Every child pitched in and helped carry all the boxes and bundles into the house. In no time at all, it seemed, the truck was empty, and the Duvitches were settled in their new home.

That was the signal for Mother to step into the kitchen. She returned carrying a basket containing a roast chicken, steaming hot, a loaf of homemade bread, and a pie. These she took to the house across the street and gave to the boy who answered her knock.

The next day when Mother was fixing lunch, we heard a faint tap at the back door. I answered it, and there, holding Mother's basket, stood a pale, dark-eyed boy in a faded shirt and patched overalls.

In the basket were the empty dishes, all of which shone, and a tiny, very shapely, potted rose tree covered with delicate pinktipped buds. It was a beautiful plant—the first of its kind to be seen in our neighborhood.

"I send them a basket of food," Mother said slowly, deeply touched, "and get this queenly gift."

She stopped to visit the Duvitches a week later. But the boy who opened the door said, "Mamma sick. She stay in bed today."

Mrs. Duvitch never came to visit us, so Mother made no further attempts to see the family. But Father disagreed when she said that she thought the Duvitches wanted their Syringa Street neighbors to leave them alone.

Syringa Street seemed to be a friendly street, but from the start the Duvitches were **marked** people. They were the one poor, struggling family in the midst of a **prosperous** community. It didn't take people long to start talking about how different they were.

At school everyone made fun of the thick black-bread sandwiches the Duvitch boys ate for lunch. And the girls stared and pointed at their boiled-out, **ragpickers'** clothes, obviously **salvaged** from the dump on the outskirts of town.

Mr. Duvitch's job in the local meatpacking plant made his walk home an **odoriferous** one. The Syringa Street youngsters, meeting him on the street, would hold their noses as he walked by.

The Duvitches' dog Kasimar behaved just like the family to which he belonged. He seemed to be afraid of his own shadow, and nobody had ever heard him bark or growl.

But Mother, remembering the potted rose tree, always had a friendly word and a smile for the young Duvitches.

....

marked set apart; visibly different
prosperous wealthy
ragpickers people who collect and sell rags and other discarded items for a living
salvaged rescued from wreckage or ruin
odoriferous bad smelling

And she always managed to find a bone for Kasimar when he scraped up the courage to **venture** across Syringa Street.

One fine Saturday in July, two years after the Duvitches had moved in, Father took Tom and me on a camping trip to Durston's Pond. The pond was only four miles north of town and was an excellent place for swimming and fishing.

We often had the quiet little pond all to ourselves. But on our arrival that afternoon we found the Duvitches in possession. Mr. Duvitch and the younger boys were casting from shore. The older sons were fishing for bass from a flat-bottomed rowboat.

....

venture to undertake or proceed in something risky

Tom and I ignored the Duvitch boys. But Father went up to Mr. Duvitch and put out his hand.

"Hello, Mr. Duvitch. It's nice to see you and the boys here."

Mr. Duvitch was a lean little man with watery blue eyes and a kicked-about look. Gratitude for being agreeably noticed showed in his face as he shook Father's hand.

"I know the mosquitoes are biting," Father went on pleasantly. "But are the fish?"

Proudly, oh so proudly, Mr. Duvitch exhibited the catch that would probably feed his family for a week. He had a fine catch of bass, perch, and sunfish, all of them alive, swimming around in the oaken washtub into which they'd been dropped.

Father told Mr. Duvitch that we couldn't hope to do as well but we'd try.

We three pitched our tent on a little hill beside the pond and rented a rowboat for the afternoon. Then Father, with a happy sigh, lay down on the blanket for a nap.

Tom and I got into our bathing suits, and for a while we stayed out in the boat, fishing. Feeling hot and sweaty later on, we rowed to shore to fetch towels and soap from the tent so we could wash.

On our way back to the water, we stopped to look at the fish still swimming around in the oaken tub. The Duvitches had moved on and were now fishing in a small arm of the pond just below us. They had their back to us and were almost out of sight.

Tom and I, our glances meeting over the big cake of soap in my hand, were similarly and wickedly tempted. We held a brief, whispered conversation. Then, egged on by Tom and quite willing on my own, I played a shameful trick on the Duvitches. Without considering further, I dropped the cake of soap into the tub of fish.

"Let's go," whispered Tom after we had watched the soap sink.

We raced back to the tent, had some sandwiches, and played ball for a while. Later on, we swam out to the deep water. Tom scrambled up on a floating log and dived off. I tried to climb on, too, but kept tumbling back into the water.

While we were splashing around, the Duvitches returned to the spot on shore where they had left their tub of fish. Soon Tom and I heard their muffled cries of disbelief and dismay.

Then we saw Father get up, walk over to them, and look down at the tub of fish near his feet. In a moment he motioned to Tom and me to come ashore at once.

Looking as guilty as we felt, we swam in and joined the group around the tub. In the midst of our stricken neighbors stood Father, holding the half-melted cake of soap in his palm.

The fish had perished miserably in the soapy water and were unfit to eat. Not only had Tom and I snatched precious food from the Duvitches' mouths, but we had also revealed the scorn we felt for them.

Father's eyes were narrow slits of blue fire in his white face. I had never seen him so angry. One look at Tom and me told him everything.

"You will begin," Father said in a voice I didn't recognize, "by saying you're sorry."

Tom and I stumbled through our apologies, trying to avoid looking at the Duvitches.

"Do you realize," Father went on coldly, "that in certain primitive communities the sort of stunt you've pulled would be punishable by death?"

We turned it over. The gray soapy water ran away in bubbly streams, disappearing into the ground. And the poisoned fish lay exposed on the grass—quiet, strangled, open-mouthed.

"Count the fish," Father ordered, his voice like steel.

Tom and I got down on our knees.

"How many are there?" demanded Father.

"Sixty-one," I said.

"How many bass?"

"Twelve."

"Get into the rowboat," Father said in the same steely tones. "You are not to come back until you've caught sixty-one fish to repay Mr. Duvitch. See to it that among them you bring in at least a dozen bass."

Father stepped up to the tent to fetch our shirts and blue jeans. Rolling them into a tight ball, he threw them angrily into the rowboat. He then turned his back on us and stalked away.

Tom and I lost no time in rowing out on the pond. We dropped anchor, threaded our steel rods, and, baiting our hooks, began to fish. I knew that if it took us all summer to catch them, we dared not set foot ashore without sixty-one fish. Almost at once Tom pulled in a good-sized bass, and ten minutes later two yellow perch were added to our string.

The **crestfallen** Duvitches went home. Father threw himself down on the blanket. That was about four in the afternoon.

Oh, the mosquitoes! They were bad enough while the light held. But as evening came on, millions of them swarmed out of the swampland surrounding the pond.

After an hour of it we wanted to leap overboard. They got in our ears, our noses, even our mouths. Nestling in our hair, they bit through to our scalps. Several times we slipped over the side of the boat, ducking under the water to escape the bloodthirsty swarms.

....

crestfallen very upset; saddened

The night dragged on while the whining clouds of mosquitoes grew thicker.

"Andy, what time is it?"

"Ten o'clock, Tom."

"Is that all?" Tom groaned. He pulled in another bass and then killed six or eight mosquitoes with one slap. Two hours passed, and midnight was ghostly on the pond.

The moon sailed high in the purple sky, casting a great white shaft of quivering radiance on the water. But sitting on a hard rowboat seat, aching with tiredness, it all seemed like a nightmare.

"Andy, what time is it?"

"Two o'clock, Tom."

The treetops whispered in the breeze. Owls hooted— mockingly, we thought—and bats circled over our heads. Our only comfort was the campfire Father kept burning near the tent. The bright flame flared like a beacon light in the dark. We went on fishing as our tormentors bit and sang.

Each hour took forever to pass, and I fairly panted for the light of dawn to come.

"Andy—"

"It's four o'clock, Tom, and we've got sixteen fish."

Dawn finally came. But a long stretch on Durston's Pond in the blistering July heat still faced us.

The rising sun cast glistening circles of rose-colored light on the windless surface of the pond. The mosquitoes thinned. The fish continued to bite, but as we fished, the sun mounted steadily. And by eleven o'clock it had become a ball of fire in the cloudless sky. Tom and I began to bake in the heat waves that shimmered over the pond.

"I wish it were night again, Andy," groaned Tom after sweating out an hour of it. "This is worse than the mosquitoes."

I tore a piece of cloth from my shirt and made it into a cap. "Take this, and cover your head, Tom," I said, handing it to him. "We might get sunstrokes and faint."

"I don't care if I do," Tom said feebly. "I'd rather be unconscious."

No breeze stirred. No cloud shadowed the pond. Even the bird life of the swamp, usually bursting with melody, was silent and motionless. Tom was drooping visibly in the glare, and I tried hard not to look at his scorched face.

Between three and four o'clock we dropped lines in a school of yellow perch and pulled up no fewer than twenty. The bass continued to bite in the deep black holes off the swamp, which bristled with tree trunks. Aching, blistered, moving like machines, Tom and I geared ourselves for the home stretch.

When the sun, dropping low, had lost its fury, and the sky began to pale, I pulled up the thirteenth bass. That bass was our sixty-first fish.

Drooping from lack of food and sleep, Tom and I rowed to shore where Father was waiting.

He received us coolly, making no comment on our condition. At once he asked to see the fish, and we held them up by the string.

"Count them," he said.

Obviously we would receive permission to land only when we had produced the required number.

"Sixty-one," said Tom, "including thirteen bass."

"Very good," said Father in businesslike tones. "We will now restore to Mr. Duvitch his rightful property."

I stumbled out of the boat, aching all over. But somehow something inside me was rejoicing. I guess that Father was secretly proud of Tom and me. And I realized, too, that all through the night he had suffered with us.

We drove in silence to the Duvitch cottage. There we found Mr. Duvitch sitting alone on the front porch.

When he saw Tom and me and we silently handed him the strings of fish, he gulped and swallowed hard. Then in a voice raw with emotion he protested that he had not wished us to suffer so.

"Will you shake hands with the boys?" asked Father.

Instead Mr. Duvitch broke down. Tom and I did not know where to look. During those moments we suffered more intensely than we had suffered in the clouds of mosquitoes and under the blazing sun. After our neighbor had **composed** himself, he seized our hands and bowed his head over them. Tom and I swallowed hard.

composed calmed; settled

Then we went home to Mother, who had heard about our **ordeal** on the pond from one of the neighbors. When she saw Tom and me she burst into tears. She tried to embrace us, but we drew back painfully. Soon she had us **plastered** with a thick coating of soothing sunburn cream.

In bed our skin stuck to the sheets and pillowcases, but we slept as if we had been drugged.

We woke up around noon the next day. "It is high time," I heard Father say calmly to Mother, "for this senseless feeling against the Duvitches to stop. And I'm willing to do my part.

"Tonight we're having supper with them. Mr. Duvitch said that since Andy and Tom caught the fish, he'd feel better if we all shared them. After a few hints from me, he invited us over. It may be a trial, but we ought to be able to bear it."

We walked across the street at six o'clock, not knowing what to expect. The Duvitches, dressed in their Sunday best, bright and shining as we had never seen them, received us as if we were royalty. They looked at Tom and me—and then delicately looked away.

I shuddered when I thought of what we would have had to endure had this been any other family.

The young Duvitches, thrilled by their first party and by the family's first acceptance in this country, kept showing

....

ordeal an extremely difficult or painful experience
plastered covered heavily and thickly, as if with plaster

their pleasure in wide, delighted smiles. I couldn't believe they were the same timid, **downcast** youngsters I had known at school.

We ate fried fish at a long plank table in the backyard. Father kept the conversation going. As he told stories and jokes, we discovered that the Duvitches had a gift for gaiety. And how they loved to laugh.

After supper David played folk songs on his accordion. Mr. Duvitch turned out to be something of a **ventriloquist**. He made the dog Kasimar talk in Polish and the cat Jan talk in German.

....

downcast sad; low-spirited
ventriloquist one who speaks without moving his lips and projects his voice to make it seem as though it is coming from somewhere else

I could tell that the Duvitch family was a great surprise to Father and that he had enjoyed the evening tremendously.

"To think," he murmured as we crossed the street, "that they should turn out to be people of courtesy and accomplishment." Father sighed and shook his head. "They're being looked down on and ignored by their inferiors."

After that evening things began to improve for the Duvitches. Our neighbors looked up to Father and often followed his lead since he was the only college graduate on Syringa Street. They decided that if the Duvitches were good enough for a highly educated man like Father, they were good enough for them. So they started inviting Mr. and Mrs. Duvitch to the community parties.

It wasn't long before the Duvitch boys and girls started making friends in the community. David was invited to play his accordion at a country dance, and he ended up being one of the town's most popular musicians.

The other Duvitch youngsters taught their folk dances to the boys and girls at school. Even Kasimar began to take on the ways of an American dog, daring to bark and growl on occasion.

Syringa Street presently had reason to be grateful to Mrs. Duvitch, who turned out to have a great gift for nursing. In times of severe illness, the doctor **invariably** suggested that she be sent for. When Mrs. Duvitch slipped into a sickroom, she never failed to bring along an air of peace. After an hour or two, the patient was calmed and the family reassured.

Soon people began to turn to the Duvitches with all kinds of problems. The elder Duvitches, with their **Old World** wisdom, would sit by the hour and talk gently and convincingly against fear, false pride, disgrace, and grief.

One winter day, Mr. Duvitch gave Father a pair of handsome, fur-lined mittens—just the right size for Father's enormous hands. After our neighbor had left, Father drew on the mittens, which had a slightly ashy odor.

"Probably one of the boys found them in an ash heap at the dump," Father remarked. "But why should I value them any the less? Who would have dreamed that the Duvitches would have so much more to offer us than we have to offer them?" ❖

---

invariably constantly; regularly without change
Old World a nickname for Europe (as distinguished from America as the "New World")

The Impact of Words

President Barack Obama's Third Annual Back-to-School Speech

September 28, 2011
Benjamin Banneker Academic High School, Washington, D.C.

Thank you. Thank you very much. Everybody, please have a seat. Well, Madam President, that was an outstanding introduction. We are so proud of Donae for representing this school so well.

And in addition, I also want to acknowledge your outstanding principal, who has been here for 20 years— first as a teacher, now as an outstanding principal—Anita Berger. Please give her a big round of applause. I want to acknowledge, as well, Mayor Gray is here—the mayor of Washington, D.C., is here. Please give him a big round of applause. And I also want to thank somebody who is going to go down in history as one of the finest Secretaries of Education that we've ever had—Arne Duncan is here.

Now, it is great to be here at Benjamin Banneker High School, one of the best high schools not only in Washington, D.C., but one of the best high schools in the country. But we've also got students tuning in from all across America. And so I want to welcome you all to the new school year, although I know that many of you already have been in school for a while. I know that here at Banneker, you've been back at school for a few weeks now. So everything is starting to settle in, just like for all your peers all across the country. The fall sports season is underway. Musicals and marching band routines are starting to shape up, I believe. And your first big tests and projects are probably just around the corner.

I know that you've also got a great deal going on outside of school. Your circle of friends might be changing a little bit. Issues that used to stay confined to hallways or locker rooms are now finding their way onto Facebook and Twitter. Some of your families might also be feeling the

President Barack Obama addressing students at Benjamin Banneker Academic High School

strain of the economy. As many of you know, we're going through one of the toughest economic times that we've gone through in our lifetime—in my lifetime. Your lifetime hasn't been that long. And so, as a consequence, you might have to pick up an after-school job to help out your family, or maybe you're babysitting for a younger sibling because mom or dad is working an extra shift.

So all of you have a lot on your plates. You guys are growing up faster and interacting with a wider world in a way that old folks like me, frankly, just didn't have to. So today, I don't want to be just another adult who stands up and lectures you like you're just kids—because you're not just kids. You're this country's future. You're young leaders. And whether we fall behind or race ahead as a nation is going to depend in large part on you. So I want to talk to you a little bit about meeting that responsibility.

It starts, obviously, with being the best student that you can be. Now, that doesn't always mean that you have to have a perfect score on every assignment. It doesn't mean that you've got to get straight As all the time—although that's not a bad goal to have. It means that you have to stay at it. You have to be determined and you have to **persevere**. It means you've got to work as hard as you know how to work. And it means that you've got to take some risks once in a while. You can't avoid the class that

persevere to continue trying to achieve something difficult

you think might be hard because you're worried about getting the best grade if that's a subject that you think you need to prepare you for your future. You've got to wonder. You've got to question. You've got to explore. And every once in a while, you need to color outside of the lines.

That's what school is for: discovering new passions, acquiring new skills, making use of this incredible time that you have to prepare yourself and give yourself the skills that you're going to need to pursue the kind of careers that you want. And that's why when you're still a student you can explore a wide range of possibilities. One hour you can be an artist; the next, an author; the next, a scientist, or a historian, or a carpenter. This is the time where you can try out new interests and test new ideas. And the more you do, the sooner you'll figure out what makes you come alive, what stirs you, what makes you excited—the career that you want to pursue.

Now, if you promise not to tell anybody, I will let you in on a little secret: I was not always the very best student that I could be when I was in high school, and certainly not when I was in middle school. I did not love every class I took. I wasn't always paying attention the way I should have. I remember when I was in eighth grade I had to take a class called ethics. Now, ethics is about right and wrong, but if you'd ask me what my favorite subject was back in eighth grade, it was basketball. I don't think ethics would have made it on the list.

But here's the interesting thing. I still remember that ethics class, all these years later. I remember the way it made me think. I remember being asked questions like: What matters in life? Or what does it mean to treat other people with dignity and respect? What does it mean to live in a diverse nation, where not everybody looks like you do, or thinks like you do, or comes from the same neighborhood as you do? How do we figure out how to get along?

Each of these questions led to new questions. And I didn't always know the right answers, but those discussions and that process of discovery—those things have lasted. Those things are still with me today. Every day, I'm thinking about those same issues as I try to lead this nation. I'm asking the same kinds of questions about, how do we as a diverse nation come together to achieve what we need to achieve? How do we make sure that every single person is treated with dignity and respect? What responsibilities do we have to people who are less fortunate than we are? How do we make sure that everybody is included in this family of Americans?

Those are all questions that date back to this class that I took back in eighth grade. And here's the thing: I still don't always know the answers to all these questions. But if I'd have just tuned out because the class sounded boring, I might have missed out on something that not only did I turn out enjoying, but has ended up serving me in good stead for the rest of my life.

So that's a big part of your responsibility, is to test things out. Take risks. Try new things. Work hard. Don't be embarrassed if you're not good at something right away. You're not supposed to be good at everything right away. That's why you're in school. The idea, though, is, is that you keep on expanding your horizons and your sense of possibility. Now is the time for you to do that. And those are also, by the way, the things that will make school more fun.

Down the road, those will be the traits that will help you succeed, as well—the traits that will lead you to invent a device that makes an iPad look like a stone tablet. Or what will help you figure out a way to use the sun and the wind to power a city and give us new energy sources that are less polluting. Or maybe you'll write the next great American novel.

Now, to do almost any of those things, you have to not only graduate from high school,—and I know I'm just—I'm in the "amen" corner with Principal Berger here—not only do you have to graduate from high school, but you're going to have to continue education after you leave. You have to not only graduate, but you've got to keep going after you graduate.

That might mean, for many of you, a four-year university. I was just talking to Donae, and she wants to be an **architect**, and she's interning with an architectural

....

architect someone who designs buildings

firm, and she's already got her sights set on what school she wants to go to. But it might, for some other folks, be a community college, or professional credentialing or training. But the fact of the matter is, is that more than 60 percent of the jobs in the next decade will require more than a high school diploma—more than 60 percent. That's the world you're walking into.

So I want all of you to set a goal to continue your education after you graduate. And if that means college for you, just getting into college is not enough. You also have to graduate. One of the biggest challenges we have right now is that too many of our young people enroll in college but don't actually end up getting their degree, and as a consequence—our country used to have the world's highest proportion of young people with a college degree; we now rank 16th. I don't like being 16th. I like being number one. That's not good enough. So we've got to use —we've got to make sure your generation gets us back to the top of having the most college graduates relative to the population of any country on earth.

If we do that, you guys will have a brighter future. And so will America. We'll be able to make sure the newest inventions and the latest breakthroughs happen right here in the United States of America. It will mean better jobs, and more fulfilling lives, and greater opportunities not only for you, but also for your kids.

So I don't want anybody who's listening here today to think that you're done once you finish high school. You are not done learning. In fact, what's happening in today's economy is—it's all about lifelong learning. You have to constantly upgrade your skills and find new ways of doing things. Even if college isn't for you, even if a four-year college isn't for you, you're still going to have to get more education after you get out of high school. You've got to start expecting big things from yourself right now.

I know that may sound a little **intimidating**. And some of you may be wondering how you can pay for college, or you might not know what you want to do with your life yet. And that's okay. Nobody expects you to have your entire future mapped out at this point. And we don't expect you to have to make it on your own. First of all, you've got wonderful parents who love you to death and want you to have a lot more opportunity than they ever had—which, by the way, means don't give them a hard time when they ask you to turn off the video games, turn off the TV and do some homework. You need to be listening to them. I speak from experience because that's what I've been telling Malia and Sasha. Don't be mad about it, because we're thinking about your future.

You've also got people all across this country—including myself and Arne and people at every level of government

....

intimidating creating a feeling of fear or uncertainty

—who are working on your behalf. We're taking every step we can to ensure that you're getting an educational system that is worthy of your potential. We're working to make sure that you have the most up-to-date schools with the latest tools of learning. We're making sure that this country's colleges and universities are affordable and accessible to you. We're working to get the best class—teachers into the classroom as well, so they can help you prepare for college and a future career.

Let me say something about teachers, by the way. Teachers are the men and women who might be working harder than just about anybody these days. Whether you go to a big school or a small one, whether you attend a public or a private or charter school—your teachers are giving up their weekends; they're waking up at dawn; they're cramming their days full of classes and extra-curricular activities. And then they're going home, eating some dinner, and then they've got to stay up sometimes past midnight, grading your papers and correcting your grammar, and making sure you got that algebra formula properly.

And they don't do it for a fancy office. They don't—they sure don't do it for the big salary. They do it for you. They do it because nothing gives them more satisfaction than seeing you learn. They live for those moments when something clicks; when you amaze them with your

intellect or your vocabulary, or they see what kind of person you're becoming. And they're proud of you. And they say, I had something to do with that, that wonderful young person who is going to succeed. They have confidence in you that you will be citizens and leaders who take us into tomorrow. They know you're our future. So your teachers are pouring everything they got into you, and they're not alone.

But I also want to emphasize this: With all the challenges that our country is facing right now, we don't just need you for the future; we actually need you now. America needs young people's passion and their ideas. We need your energy right now. I know you're up to it because I've seen it. Nothing inspires me more than knowing that young people all across the country are already making their marks. They're not waiting. They're making a difference now.

There are students like Will Kim from Fremont, California, who launched a nonprofit that gives loans to students from low-income schools who want to start their own business. Think about that. So he's giving loans to other students. He set up a non-for-profit. He's raising the money doing what he loves—through dodgeball tournaments and capture-the-flag games. But he's creative.

....

intellect intelligence

He took **initiative**. And now he's helping other young people be able to afford the schooling that they need.

There is a young man, Jake Bernstein, 17 years old, from a military family in St. Louis, worked with his sister to launch a website devoted to community service for young people. And they've held volunteer fairs and put up an online database, and helped thousands of families to find volunteer opportunities ranging from maintaining nature trails to serving at local hospitals.

And then last year, I met a young woman named Amy Chyao from Richardson, Texas. She's 16 years old, so she's the age of some of you here. During the summer, I think because somebody in her family had an illness, she decided that she was interested in cancer research. She hadn't taken chemistry yet, so she taught herself chemistry during the summer. And then she applied what she had learned and discovered a breakthrough process that uses light to kill cancer cells. Sixteen years old. It's incredible. And she's been approached by some doctors and researchers who want to work with her to help her with her discovery.

The point is you don't have to wait to make a difference. You're first obligation is to do well in school. You're first obligation is to make sure that you're preparing yourself for college and career. But you can also start making your mark right now. A lot of times young people may have

....

initiative an independent decision to take action

better ideas than us old people do anyway. We just need those ideas out in the open, in and out of the classroom.

When I meet young people like yourselves, when I sat and talk to Donae, I have no doubt that America's best days are still ahead of us, because I know the potential that lies in each of you. Soon enough, you will be the ones leading our businesses and leading our government. You will be the one who are making sure that the next generation gets what they need to succeed. You will be the ones that are charting the course of our unwritten history. And all that starts right now—starts this year.

So I want all of you who are listening, as well as everybody here at Banneker, I want you to make the most of the year that's ahead of you. I want you to think of this time as one in which you are just loading up with information and skills, and you're trying new things and you're practicing, and you're honing—all those things that you're going to need to do great things when you get out of school.

Your country is depending on you. So set your sights high. Have a great school year. Let's get to work.

Thank you very much, everybody. God bless you. God bless the United States of America. ❖

Ads: Why We Buy What We Buy

by Richard and Joyce Wolkomir

James Twitchell, a professor at the University of Florida, is visiting a Walmart. He has come with two friends, who need a new clock. But Twitchell isn't here to buy anything. He has come to gaze at the stacks of TV sets and picnic baskets and T-shirts and beach balls.

Twitchell is a professor of 19th-century poetry. But these days he studies products in stores—backpacks, computer games, kitty litter, basketball sneakers, light bulbs, wristwatches . . . . It fascinates him that we have so many products on sale. Zillions of them. Never before in history have people had so much to buy.

Suppose you lived 500 years ago. Even if you were a king or queen, even if you were super rich, you could not buy a box of Cheerios. There *were* no Cheerios. Today, *anyone* can buy Cheerios and other products (as long as he or she has money). Not only that, but you get to choose what you buy. In the drugstore, there are not just three kinds of shampoo or nine kinds: there are *hundreds* of kinds of shampoo. And Twitchell wonders: How do we choose among so much stuff to buy?

That's why he's fascinated by advertisements. They are how people who sell products try to persuade us to buy them. Ads come at us all the time—from TV, radio, magazines and newspapers, web pages, even the sides of city buses.

Twitchell has learned that each of us sees or hears about 3,000 ads every day. With so many ads zinging at us, he wonders how any particular ad gets our attention. And how does it persuade us to buy, say a certain brand of sunglasses? So Twitchell is checking out Walmart, figuring out how the store persuades us to buy things.

"Look at this huge wire shopping cart," he says. "It's so roomy you don't feel you're buying too much—people who specialize in thinking up ways to get us to buy products fooled around with the size of these carts, getting them just right!"

Twitchell began studying products and advertising 15 years ago, when he was teaching about poetry: "I suddenly realized my students had no interest in what I had to say!" But his students could flawlessly recite the contents of a Big Mac: two all-beef patties, special sauce, lettuce, cheese, pickles, and onions on a sesame-seed bun.

Twitchell was stunned: "I wanted to know why the stuff they knew was so powerful it pushed my stuff out of the way."

Since then, he has been observing himself, his family, his **colleagues**, his students, his neighbors. He has invited himself into advertising agencies to see how the writers and artists who work there think up ads. He has explored

colleagues members of the same profession

advertising's history. And he's written about the impact of all that selling of products in such books as *Lead Us Into Temptation: The Triumph of American Materialism* and *Twenty Ads That Shook the World*.

Twitchell finds that modern society, where so much of our attention is on selling products and buying them, got its start in the **Industrial Revolution** of the 1800s. Before that, workers using hand tools made most products, whether it was spoons or shirts. But then newly invented machines began turning out products in vast numbers, from sewing needles to dishes. "Until the Industrial Revolution only the wealthy had things—now the rest of us are having a go at arranging our lives around things," Twitchell says. Young people in particular now have lots more money to spend, and many ads are aimed right at them.

Advertising's job is subtler than just urging, "Buy this!" Twitchell likes to quote an advertising executive from the 1950s, Rosser Reeves, who would hold up two quarters. Advertising, said Reeves, must make you believe those two quarters are different. In fact, the ad had to persuade you that one of those quarters was *worth more*.

Twitchell traces advertising's rise to—believe it or not—the making of soap by machines. "The manufacture of soap is a turning point in civilization," he says. Originally, farmers made soap by molding animal fats into balls,

<hr />

Industrial Revolution the introduction of machines that changed the way goods were produced

which eventually stank. With the machine age came better soap, pressed into bars that lasted forever. But one soap was much like another.

In 1881, at James Gamble's soap factory in Cincinnati, a worker forgot to turn off the mixing machines: Accidentally, he produced a batch of soap so air-filled it floated. Gamble claimed his new soap floated because it was pure—in fact, he claimed it was 99 $^{44}/_{100}$ percent pure. He gave his new soap a name: Ivory.

Meanwhile, in England, Andrew Pears had developed a soap that looked different because it was clear, instead of white or colored. When Pears's son-in-law, Thomas J. Barratt,

What started it all: the first (long-winded) Ivory soap ad, 1882

took over, he plastered his company's slogan on walls all over the British Empire: "Good Morning! Have You Used Your Pears' Soap?"

Before that, soap was just soap. Like biscuits or nails, it came in barrels. To get some, you told the store clerk,

"Two bars of soap, please." But now soap had a name—a "brand." It might be Ivory soap. Or it might be Pears' soap. A manufacturer could put ads in newspapers urging people to ask for soap by name. Now, nudged by advertising that said clear soap was best, you might specify, "Pears' soap, please." Or if an ad had convinced you soap that floats in your bathtub is best, you might say, "Ivory soap, please."

Decisions, decisions…what soap should I buy? A Pears' soap ad from 1886

Twitchell, in the Walmart, peers at a barrel displaying kitchen floor mats. "Two for five dollars!" he says, reading a sign. It is clearly tempting. But he pulls himself away to note that people are starting to use the things they buy to advertise *themselves*. Suppose, for instance, that all brands of scooter are pretty much the same. But advertisements suggest that only really cool people use a certain brand of scooter. You insist on buying that cool brand: You want people to think you must be cool because you have the cool scooter.

Twitchell says we have so many products and so much advertising, they actually have helped shape the way we live. For instance, we have a two-day weekend in part because the Industrial Revolution produced so many products that people needed more time for shopping. And so workers got Saturday off. Says Twitchell: "It's become shopping day at the mall."

Today's idea of what Santa Claus looks like began in the 1920s, because Coca-Cola's sales slumped in winter. Ads began showing Santa—in his modern costume—drinking a Coke. Rudolph the Red-Nosed Reindeer first appeared in the 1930s, in a Montgomery Ward advertisement. Kodak ads made birthday-cake candles popular: ads pictured people at birthday parties, blowing out candles, to show what you could do with Kodak film and a Kodak camera.

Twitchell points out that cereal is now a standard breakfast food because decades ago the Post and Kellogg

Would you trust this man's taste in soft drinks? Coca-Cola helping define Santa, in an ad from 1955

companies developed packaged cold cereals. Then they used advertisements to persuade people to buy them. Earlier, breakfast had meant finishing last night's dinner. Leftovers went to the family dog. Now we have "dog food," which Twitchell traces to ads pushing what was then a new product from the Ralston Purina company.

Twitchell is no longer amazed that his students—taking in thousands of advertisements every day—decide what they think about each other based on what products they buy. His students even refer to certain classmates as "Gaps," after the retail chain where they buy their clothes.

Much of what we buy, says Twitchell, we buy to impress others. Between ages 15 and 25, he notes, we are particularly eager to spend our money, on everything from just the right haircut to just the right jeans, because boys want to impress girls and vice versa. It is, says Twitchell, much like male birds showing off their brightly colored feathers to females. However, the urge wanes. By age 45 or so, most people begin

A Ralston ad from the 1930s

losing interest in buying so much. And that is why ads and TV shows focus ferociously on youths.

"Why," asks Twitchell, "are my daughters willing to buy a bottle of water worth two cents and pay $1.50?" It is because, he says, they are not buying the water itself. They are buying the values—such as being hip—that advertising has attached to particular brands of bottled water.

It works. Today's average American consumes twice as many goods and services as in 1950. Today's average home is twice as large as a post-World War II home. A decade ago, most grocery scores stocked about 9,000 items; today's stores carry some 24,000.

As his friends prepare to leave the Walmart, having failed to find the clock they sought, Twitchell stops. "I'm going to go buy the floor mats I saw back there, but after you leave, because I'm ashamed to be seen giving in to that two-for-the price-of-one deal," he says.

Even so, Twitchell believes the stuff cramming our stores, which advertisements strain to get us to buy, is not necessarily harmful. "After all," he says, "we don't call them 'bads'—we call them 'goods!'" ❖

Richard and Joyce Wolkomir are a husband-and-wife writing team. They live in Vermont with their writing "assistant," Nosmo King, a Welsh corgi. Nosmo loves advertisements for kibbles.

Index of Authors and Titles

Acknowledgments

"The Stone" from THE FOUNDLING AND OTHER TALES OF PRYDAIN by Lloyd Alexander. Copyright © 1973 by Lloyd Alexander. Reprinted by permission of Henry Holt and Company, LLC.

"Kaddo's Wall" from THE COW-TAIL SWITCH AND OTHER WEST AFRICAN STORIES by Harold Courlander and George Herzog. Copyright 1947, © 1974 by Harold Courlander. Reprinted by permission of Henry Holt and Company, LLC.

"Zlateh the Goat" from STORIES FOR CHILDREN by Isaac Bashevis Singer. Copyright © 1984 by Isaac Bashevis Singer. Reprinted by permission of Farrar, Strauss, and Giroux, LLC.

"The Black Snake" by Patricia Hubbell, From 8 A.M. SHADOWS by Patricia Hubbell. Copyright © 1965, 1993 by Patricia Hubbell. Used by permission by Marian Reiner for the author.

"A Narrow Fellow in the Grass" from THE POEMS OF EMILY DICKINSON, edited by Thomas H. Johnson, Cambridge, Mass.: The Belknap Press of Harvard University Press, Copyright © 1951, 1955 by the President and Fellows of Harvard College. Copyright © renewed 1979, 1983 by the President and Fellows of Harvard College. Copyright © 1914, 1918, 1919, 1924, 1929, 1930, 1932, 1935, 1937, 1942 by Martha Dickinson Bianchi. Copyright © 1952, 1957, 1958, 1963, 1965 by Mary L. Hampson.

"Stray" by Cynthia Rylant from EVERY LIVING THING by Cynthia Rylant, copyright © 1985 by Cynthia Rylant, reprinted by permission of Simon and Schuster Books for Young Readers, an imprint of Simon and Schuster Children's Publishing Division.

"Perseus and the Quest for Medusa's Head," "The Adventures of Theseus," and "Atalanta, the Fleet-Footed Huntress" adapted from OLD GREEK STORIES by James Baldwin (New York: American Book Company, 1895).

"The Legend of Damon and Pythias" by Fan Kissen from THE BAG OF FIRE AND OTHER PLAYS by Fan Kissen. Copyright © 1964 by Houghton Mifflin Company, copyright renewed © 1993 by John Kissen Heaslip. Reprinted by permission of Houghton Mifflin Comany. All rights reserved.

"The Difficult Path" from FLYING LESSONS AND OTHER STORIES. Text copyright © 2017 by Grace Lin. Reprinted by permission of Writers House LLC acting as agent for the author.

"Tears of Autumn" from THE FORBIDDEN STITCH by Yoshiko Uchida. The Estate of Yoshiko Uchida c/o The Bancroft Library, Administrative Offices. Copyright © 1989 by Yoshiko Uchida.

Image Credits

318 Portrait of the Italian artist Raphael. © North Wind Picture Archives/Alamy. 324 Mary Cassatt. © Pictorial Press Ltd/Alamy. 329 *Little Girl in a Blue Armchair* by Mary Cassatt. © Artokoloro Quint Lox Limited/Alamy. 331 Portrait of Marian Anderson. © Michael Ochs Archives/Getty Images. 338 Marian Anderson singing on the steps of the Lincoln Memorial. © Hulton Archive/Getty Images. 343 Marian Anderson and President Jimmy Carter. © dpa picture alliance/Alamy. 344 Mahatma Gandhi. © World History Archive/Alamy. 349 Mahatma Gandhi participating in the Salt March. © Universal History Archive/Universal Images Group/Getty Images. 352 Portrait of Supreme Court Justice Thurgood Marshall. © Bachrach/Getty Images. 359 Thurgood Marshall outisde the Supreme Court. © Hank Walker/The LIFE Picture Collection/Getty Images. 363 Student Linda Brown with her class in Topeka, Kansas. © Carl Iwasaki/The LIFE Picture Collection/Getty Images. 369 President John F. Kennedy speaking on space exploration. © NASA Photo/Alamy. 373 First Lady Michelle Obama speaking in Belfast, Northern, Ireland. © Peter Macdiarmid/Getty Images. 376 Smart phone with Donation on the screen. © CarmenMurillo/iStock. 378 Unknown caller. © Vesalainen/iStock. 388 Blue suede shoes. © sashi/Shutterstock. 392 Senior man. © diego_cervo/iStock. 401 President Barack Obama, First Lady Michelle Obama, and their daughter Malia Obama, meet with Malala Yousafzai in the Oval Office. © Pete Souza/The White House/Getty Images. 402 President Barack Obama speaks with Indian child rights activist and 2014 Nobel Peace Prize winner Kailash Satyarthi. © Saul LoebAFP/Getty Images. 405 Pakistani activist and Nobel Peace Prize laureate Malala Yousafzai. © Abdul Majeed/AFP/Getty Images. 415 Two boys fishing. © Bettmann/Getty Images. 417 Fish. © MarkLinnard/iStock. 424 Family picnic. © Corbis/Getty Images. 429 President Barack Obama speaking to students. © Mandel Ngan/AFP/Getty Images. 443 Ivory Soap. © Science History Images/Alamy. 444 Pears' Soap advertisement. © Pictorial Press Ltd/Alamy. 445 Coca-Cola advertisement from 1955. © Jeff Morgan 16/Alamy. 446 Ralston Cereal advertisement. © Chronicle/Alamy

Illustration Credits

All illustrations © K12 unless otherwise noted.
10, 32, 208–209, 237 Lael Henderson. **159, 162** Line drawings by Willy Pogany, from *The Golden Fleece and the Heroes Who Lived Before Achilles* by Padraic Colum (New York: Macmillan, 1921).